DESERTS ON THE MARCH

Deserts on

PAUL B. Bigelow SEARS

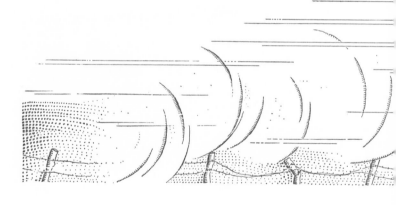

the March

UNIVERSITY OF OKLAHOMA PRESS

NORMAN

TO *The Master and Mistress* OF
Rosedale Cottage

A Word from the Author

Deserts on the March was written and published in 1935. Since then world affairs have moved with increasing speed. A cataclysmic world war accompanied a moist swing of the climatic cycle during the 1940's, followed by successive years of drought in the early 1950's. An unexpected rise in the American birth rate beginning during the 1940's has upset the prediction of demographers that population would presently stabilize at somewhere around 160,000,000.

Soil conservation measures inaugurated during the 1930's, other technological advances, and a subsidy plan devised to relieve rural hardship have resulted in gross overproduction of food and other agricultural crops. Although a majority of the world's human beings are ill fed, the threat of hunger in this country seems indefinitely postponed. Yet living costs have risen steadily. The increasing cost of food necessitates higher industrial wages, while increasing manufacturing costs mean rising expenses to the farmer. These circumstances, coupled with staggering expenditures for defense, have brought on an unwelcome inflation.

Accompanying these and other complex developments there has been a discernible interest in the proper management of our environment. Often it has been sparked by acute situations, notably in the case of water. Yet countering this interest has been the widespread growth of a feeling that science and technology will resolve any real emergency and bring us to a condition of effortless plenty. New mouths are too often looked on merely as new customers, while one hears frequent talk of a perpetually expanding economy. Science, warmly embraced as an aid of profit, convenience, and comfort, is not welcomed as a source of perspective.

The essential thesis of *Deserts on the March* is that man, inseparably a part of the natural world and dependent upon it, has now become a responsible natural force. His present actions will shape the future as those of the past are shaping the present. Events and observations of a subsequent quarter-century have done nothing to modify this principle. Rather they have served to confirm it.

Long ago John Stuart Mill, in a neglected chapter, "The Stationary State," pointed out the ultimate necessity of an equilibrium between society and environment—a concept amply sustained by rules of experience in the physical and biological sciences. Such an equilibrium can be attained in two ways—either under the grim pressure of crisis or by the conscious, responsible forethought of a free people. The Western world recognizes in principle the ethic of love and compassion toward fellow-man. If this be expanded as it should to include the unborn no less than the living, we need not fear any lack of political, economic, or technical means to make it effective. Is it too much to ask that every child of the future has a right not only to be welcomed but to inherit a reasonable chance at the good life?

Paul B. Sears

New Haven, Conn.
July 30, 1959

Introduction

This book is one of the important contributions to the life and economy of this nation. Its author is not only a distinguished botanist; he is a first-rate ecologist, a genuine economist, an agriculturist of no mean skill. In short, he belongs to the small category of men of whom we have so great a need in this specialist-ridden civilization, a man who understands that merely building a dam does not solve the problems of flood, of water supply; a man who does not believe that subsidies and the lavish and indiscriminate expenditures of government money on improvised projects help the condition of a family living on a miserable diet, upon impoverished soil devoid of the elements which are necessary to human intelligence, energy, and life. Paul Sears is a thinker of broad culture in the sense of true culture, which means not merely the knowledge of facts or intensive training in a single field but a broad knowledge covering many fields and an understanding of facts and their relation to each other. That is why this book as a book and Dr. Sears as a thinker are of great importance to us.

Few books have done so much to bring to the attention of the American people the terrible results to our economy and civilization of the shameful waste of our natural resources and of the even more appalling results which lie ahead of us if the nation does not change its course. The cost of the world wars I and II and of the armed truce separating them can never be measured in terms of *money*, for money is only a variable. A dollar may be worth one hundred cents today and one cent tomorrow. Its real value is determined by what it will buy and by the value of the natural resources which support it and the national power and wealth which grow out of these resources. We can measure the *real* cost of this war only in terms of the number of trees we have cut down, by the amount of minerals we have processed and shipped out of the country, by the amount of agricultural land we have worn out or permitted to wash away, by the lowered intelligence and vitality of people reduced to a diet deficient in proteins and minerals, by the number of our vigorous and intelligent young men killed or maimed.

We have had too much thinking and action in terms of money and too little in terms of real wealth. Dr. Hugh Bennett of the U. S. Soil Conservation Service is responsible for one statement which is beyond dispute—that "this nation and civilization is founded upon nine inches of topsoil and when that is gone there will be no longer any nation or any civilization." And who can dispute the hypothesis that when our natural resources are gone we shall cease to be a nation of either wealth or power.

We have wasted our heritage recklessly and in consequence the level of our standard of living is being depressed to the level of that of less fortunate nations. Once we boasted that there was no peasant population in America. Today we have millions of people in villages and agricultural areas living below the standard of European peasants and at least a million or two living at the level of Chinese peasants. In some southern agricultural states the average cash income of agricultural areas is $128.00 a year. The reason arises not from high transportation costs, or distance from markets, or in any purely economic source, but from exhausted and eroded soils and a miserable agriculture.

In this book Dr. Sears is writing of what are perhaps the most important factors in our national existence. They are of the utmost importance to every citizen, most of all perhaps to the residents of our monstrous, unplanned, industrial cities, to our bankers and industrialists seeking markets for money and manufactured goods and to the working man, haunted always by the spectre of depressions and unemployment. Do not think, reader, that none of this concerns you. It affects directly your income, your taxes, your living costs and the very health of yourself and your children.

Deserts on the March will continue to open new horizons of thought; and a nation without thinking citizens is as doomed as a nation without topsoil or forests or oil. I urge you to read this excellent book and then do something about the problems of which it treats.

Louis Bromfield

Malabar Farm
Lucas, Ohio, April 15, 1947

The Chapters

DESERTS ON THE MARCH

The face of earth is a graveyard, and so it has always been. To earth each living thing restores when it dies that which has been borrowed to give form and substance to its brief day in the sun. From earth, in due course, each new living being receives back again a loan of that which sustains life. What is lent by earth has been used by countless generations of plants and animals now dead and will be required by countless others in the future. The supply of an element such as phosphorus is so limited that if it were not constantly being returned to the soil, a single century would be sufficient to produce a disastrous reduction in the amount of life. No plant or animal, nor any sort of either, can establish permanent right of possession to the materials which compose its physical body.

Left to herself, nature manages these loans and redemptions in not unkindly fashion. She maintains a balance which will permit the briefest time to elapse between burial and renewal. The turnover of material for new generations to use is steady and regular. Wind and water, those twin sextons, do their work gently. Each type of plant and animal, so far as it is fit, has its segment of activity and can bring forth its own kind to the limits of subsistence. The red rule of tooth and claw is less harsh in fact than in seeming. There is a balance in undisturbed nature between food and feeder, hunter and prey, so that the resources of the earth are never idle. Some plants or animals may seem to dominate the rest, but they do so only so long as the general balance is maintained. The whole world of living things exists as a series of communities

whose order and permanence shame all but the most successful of human enterprises.

It is into such an ordered world of nature that primitive
man fits as a part. A family of savage man, living by the chase
and gathering wild plants, requires a space of ten to fifty
square miles for subsistence. If neighbors press too closely, the
tomahawk of tribal warfare offers a rude but perhaps merci-
ful substitute for starvation. Man in such a stage takes what he
can get on fairly even terms with the rest of nature. Wind and
water may strike fear to his heart and even wreak disaster
upon him, but on the whole their violence is tempered. The
forces of nature expend themselves beneficently upon the
highly developed and well-balanced forests, grasslands, even
desert. To the greatest possible extent the surface consists of
mellow, absorbent soil, anchored and protected by living
plants—a system buffered against the caprice of the elements,
although of course subject to slow and orderly change. Bare
ground left by the plow will have as much soil washed off in
ten years as the unbroken prairie will lose in four thousand.
Even so, soil in the prairie will be forming as fast as, or faster
than it is lost.

Living in such a setting, man knows little or nothing of
nature's laws, yet conforms to them with the perfection over
which he has no more choice than the oaks and palms, the cats
and reptiles around him. Gradually, however, and with many
halting steps, man has learned enough about the immutable
laws of cause and effect so that with tools, domestic animals,
and crops he can speed up the processes of nature tremendously along certain lines. The rich Nile Valley can be made to
support, not one, but one thousand people per square mile, as
it does today. Cultures develop, cities and commerce flourish,
hunger and fear dwindle as progress and the conquest of nature expand. Unhappily, nature is not so easily thwarted. The
old problems of population pressure and tribal warfare appear
in newer and more horrible guise, with whole nations trained
for slaughter. And back of it all lies the fact that man has upset

[4]

the balance under which wind and water were beneficial agents of construction, releasing them as twin demons which carve the soil from beneath his feet, to hasten the decay and burial of his handiwork.

Nature is not to be conquered save on her own terms. She is not conciliated by cleverness or industry in devising means to defeat the operation of one of her laws through the workings of another. She is a very business-like old lady, who plays no favorites. Man is welcome to out-number and dominate the other forms of life, provided he can maintain order among the relentless forces whose balanced operation he has disturbed. But this hard condition is one which, to date, he has scarcely met. His own past is full of clear and somber warnings—vanished civilizations buried, like dead flies in lacquer, beneath their own dust and mud.

For man, who fancies himself the conqueror of it, is at once the maker and the victim of the wilderness. Even the dense and hostile jungles of the tropics are often the work of his hands. The virgin forest of the tropics, as of other climes, is no thicket of scrub and thorn, but a cathedral of massive, well-spaced giant trees under whose dense canopy the alien and tangled rabble of the jungle does not thrive. Order and permanence are here—these giants bring forth young after their own kind, but only so fast as death and decay break the solid ranks of the elders. Let man clear these virgin forests, even convert them into fields, he can scarcely keep them. Nature claims them again, and her advance guards are the scrambled barriers through which man must chop his way.

In the early centuries of the present era, while the Roman Empire was cracking to pieces, the Mayas built great cities in Central America. Their huge pyramids, massive masonry, and elaborate carving are proof of capacity and leisure. They also indicate that the people who built them probably felt a sense of security, permanence, and accomplishment as solid as our own. To them the end of their world was no doubt unthinkable save as a device of priestly dialectic, or an exercise of the romantic imagination. Food there was in abundance, furnished by the maize, cacao, beans, and a host of other plants of which southern Mexico is the first home. Fields were easily cleared by girdling trees with sharp stone hatchets. You can write your name on plate glass with their little jadeite chisels. The dead trees were then, as they are today in Yucatan, destroyed by fire, and crops were planted in their ashes.

Yet by the sixth century all of this was abandoned and the Second Empire established northward in Yucatan, to last with varying fortunes until the Spanish conquest. Pyramids and stonework became the playground of the jungle, so hidden and bound beneath its knotted mesh that painful labor has been required to reveal what is below. Farther north in Yucatan, in humble villages, are the modern people, unable to read the hieroglyphs of their ancestors, and treasuring only fragments of the ancient lore which have survived by word of mouth. There persists among these people, for example, a considerable body of knowledge concerning medicinal plants, their properties and mode of use. But the power and glory of the cities is gone. In their place are only ruins and wilderness. Their world, once so certain, stable, dependable, and definite, is gone. And why?

Here, of course, is a first-rate mystery for modern skill and knowledge to unravel. The people were not exterminated, nor their cities taken over by an enemy. Plagues may cause temporary migrations, but not the permanent abandonment of established and prosperous centers. The present population to the north has its share of debilitating infections, but its ancestors were not too weak or wasted to establish the Second Empire after they left the First. Did the climate in the abandoned cities become so much more humid that the invasion of dense tropical vegetation could not be arrested, while fungous pest, insects, and diseases took increasing toll? This is hard to prove. Were the inhabitants starved out because they had no steel tools or draft animals to break the heavy sod which formed over their resting fields? Many experts think so.

Certainly the soil of the wet tropics is very different from the deep rich black soil of the prairies. Just as soaking removes salt from a dried mackerel, so the nourishing minerals are quickly removed from these soils by the abundant water. In the steaming hot climate the plant and animal materials which fall upon the ground are quickly rotted, sending gases into the air and losing much of what is left, in the pounding, soaking wash of the heavy tropical rains. Such organic material as may be present is well incinerated when the forest covering is killed and burned, as it was by the ancient Mayas, and still is by their descendants. Such a clearing will yield a heavy crop for a few seasons, by virtue of the fertilizer in the ashes and what little is left in the soil. Presently the yield must decline to the point where cultivation is no longer possible. A fresh clearing is made and the old one abandoned. Step by step the cultivation proceeds farther from the place of beginning. Whether the idle fields, forming an ever widening border about the great cities, came to be hidden beneath an armor of impenetrable turf or completely ruined by sheet erosion and puddling, is immaterial. The restoration of fertility by idleness has proved a failure even in temperate climates. It is not a matter of one, or even several, human generations, but a process of centuries. The cities of the Mayas were doomed by the very system that gave them birth. Man's conquest of nature was an illusion, however brilliant. Like China before the Manchu invaders, or Russia in the face of Napoleon, the jungle seemed to yield and recede before the Mayas, only to turn with deadly, relentless deliberation and strangle them.

So much for a striking case of failure in the New World. How about the Old—the cradle of humanity? Here there are striking cases of apparent success, long continued, such as eastern China and the Nile Valley. On the other hand are many instances of self-destruction as dramatic as that of the Mayas—for example the buried cities of the Sumerian desert. Let us examine both failure and seeming success; after we have done so, we shall realize how closely they are interwoven.

The invention of flocks and herds of domestic animals enabled man to increase and prevail throughout the great grassy and even the desert interior of the Old World. Food and wealth could be moved on the hoof. A rough and ready "cow-puncher" psychology was developed as a matter of course, combining a certain ruthless capacity for quick action along with an aversion to sustained and methodical labor, except for women. Living as these people did, in a region where water was none too abundant and pasture not always uniform, movement was necessary. Normally this was a seasonal migration—a round trip like that of the buffalo and other wild grazing animals. But from time to time the combination of events brought about complete and extensive shifts.

Where moisture was more abundant, either directly from rain, or indirectly through huge rivers, another invention took place. This second invention was the cultivation of certain nutritious grasses with unusually large fruits—the cereals. Probably not far from the mouth of the Yangtze River in southeastern China rice was domesticated, while at the eastern end of the Mediterranean wheat and barley were put to similar use, both in Irak (Mesopotamia) and Egypt. Along with these cereals many other plants, such as beans, clover, alfalfa, onions, and the like were grown. This invention provided food cheaply and on a hitherto unprecedented scale. Domestic animals could now be penned, using their energy to make flesh and milk instead of running it off in the continued movement for grass and water. Other animals like the cat and dog relieved man of the necessity of guarding his stored wealth against the raids of rats and robbers. Large animals like the ox and ass saved him the labor of carriage and helped in threshing and tillage. The people themselves became accustomed to methodical and prolonged labor. They devised means of storage and transport and developed commerce. Mechanical contrivances proved useful and were encouraged. On the other hand such folk were not celebrated for their aggressiveness nor for an itching foot. As they became organized and accumulated a surplus of skill and energy they developed great cities and other public works, with all adornments.

The history of early civilization can be written largely in terms of these two great inventions in living—the pastoral life of the dry interior and the settled agriculture of the well-watered regions. Their commerce, warfare, and eventual, if imperfect, combination make the western Europe of today. What of their effects upon the land?

Wherever we turn, to Asia, Europe, or Africa, we shall find the same story repeated with an almost mechanical regularity. The net productiveness of the land has been decreased. Fertility has been consumed and soil destroyed at a rate far in excess of the capacity of either man or nature to replace. The glorious achievements of civilization have been builded on borrowed capital to a scale undreamed by the most extravagant of monarchs. And unlike the bonds which statesmen so blithely issue to—and against—their own people, an obligation has piled up which cannot be repudiated by the stroke of any man's pen.

Uniformly the nomads of the interior have crowded their great ranges to the limit. We shall see later what a subtle matter this crowding may be—the fields may look as green as ever, until the inevitable drier years come along. Then the soil becomes exposed, to be blown away by wind, or washed into great flooded rivers during the infrequent, usually torrential rains. The cycle of erosion gains momentum, at times conveying wealth to the farmer downstream in the form of rich black soil, but quite as often destroying and burying his means of livelihood beneath a coat of sterile mud.

The reduction of pasture, even with the return of better years, dislocates the scheme of things for the owners of flocks and herds. Raids, mass migrations, discouraged and feeble attempts at agriculture, or, rarely, the development of irrigation and dry farming result—and history is made.

Meanwhile, in the more densely settled regions of cereal farming, population pressure demands every resource to maintain yield. So long as rich mud is brought downstream in thin layers at regular intervals, the valleys yield good returns at the expense of the continental interior. But such imperial gifts are hard to control, increasingly so as occupation and overgrazing upstream develop. In the course of events farming spreads from the valley to the upland. The forests of the upland are stripped, both for their own product and for the sake of the ground which they occupy. Growing cities need lumber, as well as food. For a time these upland forest soils of the moister regions yield good crops, but gradually they too are exhausted. Imperceptibly sheet erosion moves them into the valleys, with only temporary value to the latter. Soon the rich black valley soil is overlaid by pale and unproductive material from the uplands. The latter may become an abandoned range of gullies, or in rarer cases human resourcefulness may come to the fore, and by costly engineering works combined with agronomic skill, defer the final tragedy of abandonment.

Thus have we sketched, in broad strokes to be sure, the story of man's destruction upon the face of his own Mother Earth. The story on the older continents has been a matter of millenia, as we shall see. In North America it has been a matter of not more than three centuries at most—generally a matter of decades. Mechanical invention plus exuberant vitality have accomplished the conquest of a continent with unparalleled speed, but in doing so have broken the gentle grip wherein nature holds and controls the forces which serve when restrained, destroy when unleashed.

The Wisdom of the Ages

Is the battle really a losing one to date? Have not invention, energy, and discipline consolidated the gains of mankind securely against all danger, excepting our own selfishness and capacity for mutual destruction in time of war and peace? What of the wisdom of the East? What of the vast plain of eastern China, which feeds one-quarter of the human race? What of Mother India, whose peoples have increased under British rule? What of the narrow valley of the Nile, as populous, and seemingly as fertile as ever? Are not these the reality, with man in equilibrium with nature as long as both shall last? Are not the cases of retreat and destruction mere incidents, inconclusive and temporary?

China is larger than the United States of America, and more diverse. Her people are as clever in handling the land as any. She has, in a literal sense, forgotten more than the West ever knew. To her the West is indebted for rice, the peach, the soy bean, alfalfa. From her southern boundaries came the apple, which even today forms wild mountain forests in the Himalayas. Her emperors maintained peace and communication between her provinces for long periods. New varieties of many plants were developed and their culture spread. It is said, and probably with truth, that the land of southeastern China is almost unique in bringing forth as heavy yields today as it ever has. Her people are industrious, frugal, and intelligent. If allowed to come here and compete, they could drive our thriftiest farmers out of business. What of China?

To begin with, China contains millions of people who are never far from the verge of starvation. Nearly every year of her history witnesses some flood or famine, even though local in character. When seven thousand Chinese Communists were wiped out in four days the government reminded its critics, truly enough, that the cost in lives of this particular project in "political sanitation" was a small matter beside the deaths in a single provincial famine. Every foot of tillable land throughout most of China is terraced and contoured with geometrical perfection. Her farmers save every scrap of garbage and other organic matter. They trudge long distances to the cities and villages with containers across their shoulders, to bring back to their farms what the writers on agriculture call by the euphemistic name of "night soil"—human excrement. All of this, together with the black rich ooze retrieved from their rivers following high water, is worked into their tiny fields with more pains than a Dutch housewife bestows upon her window garden. In some way, too, the Chinese farmer has learned the value of legumes in improving the soil. Unlike the Europeans, who knew it in the days of Rome, but neglected it thereafter, he has consistently practiced legume rotation, growing among other things soy beans, from which Chinese cooks evolve an imposing array of edibles. All of this is not to say that Chinese agriculture is perfect—it has much to learn from modern science. For example, the importance of seed selection is not properly understood, and inferior varieties of plants are often grown. But the fact remains that the general standard of practice is so far above that in many parts of the Western world as to admit no comparison. One of the finest achievements of the Chinese farmer has been the conversion of the Red Basin of Szechuan from an incipient bad land, supporting less than a hundred forty-five thousand people in 1710, into a flourishing, beautifully terraced agricultural countryside of forty-five million inhabitants.

Yet nothing is more mistaken than to think that China is in any real sense self-sustaining. She is using fertility stored by the work of her great rivers during millions of years past, supplemented by present tribute of an area twice the size of

China proper, but with one-sixteenth as many people. In fact her two great rivers, the Yangtze and the Hwang, rise in Tibet, with its sparse population of less than three people to a square mile. These streams are fed by seemingly inexhaustible snows, and bear mineral matter, along with vegetable material afforded by the world's largest mountains and their lush plant cover. Let modern industry penetrate to these sources and exploit them with the zeal that has been expended upon our own Rocky Mountains, and China proper is doomed.

Without doubt the production of these upper watersheds is more a matter of happy chance than of deliberate policy. If means existed for the ready transport and marketing of their timber, it doubtless would have been stripped before now. As it is, the pressure of population continually surges against these forested mountains. Some decades ago potatoes were introduced into western China by the missionary priests in the hope that they would provide an additional insurance against recurring famine. As in western Europe when first introduced, the potato was regarded by the Chinese with contempt, as an inferior food suitable only for those who could not do better by themselves. Its cultivation was not too efficiently managed. Now the potato probably originated in the Andean highlands of South America, and can thrive at higher elevations than most of the staple food crops of western China. When this fact was discovered, there was a rush to strip the forests and replace them with potato patches. Eventually—in fact, very shortly—the same thing happened that took place when the Irish became too dependent upon the potato. The fields were blighted by disease. No other crop afforded reserves, and the land so recently put to use had to be abandoned. This occurred on the upper valley of the Yangtze, where climatic conditions favor the quick return of the forest. But let such efforts continue and not even the genial climate of southern China will suffice to protect the upper valley against serious erosion, and the lower Yangtze against destructive flood.

Unlike the Yangtze, the Hwang, or Yellow River, is notorious for its disastrous floods. Starting, too, in the snowy, wooded, sparsely peopled mountains of Tibet, it flows down through a drier, more continental region than its southern fellow. Much of its upper valley is plateau, not unlike our high plains of the West. Here the pressure of population has been insistent. Herds and flocks have taxed the pastures to their limit, and cultivation has been attempted wherever possible. But in such a climate there is no friendly surplus of atmospheric moisture to encourage the speedy return of vegetation, once it is destroyed. Conditions here have favored the destructive action of wind and water, doubtless long before the advent of man upon the scene. Whatever plant life there is to anchor the soil is present, as in the high plains of our own country, only by the grace of unceasing struggle throughout the ages.

In consequence much of the Hwang Valley is today a region in which raging flood alternates with blinding dust storms. The infrequent but torrential rains carve the landscape and bear their toll of yellow mud into the stream and down into the populous lowland. Drought follows, and the denuded face of the landscape becomes the plaything of the ever-blowing winds. The damage is perhaps aggravated by the fact that much of the soil was originally brought in by wind from the Gobi Desert and elsewhere, during periods of arid climate. Such soil, known as *loess*, is very abundant in Asia, covering, it is estimated, about 3 per cent of the continent. Although very fertile when supplied with water, it forms vertical cliffs when eroded, and is speedily converted into a fantastic region of bad lands, unsuitable for any use. Lying quite outside the area of true climatic desert in Asia, we thus have extensive areas of cultural, or man-made desert, not only useless in themselves, but a menace to the fertile, well-watered plains to the east, downstream.

It should be clear then that the face of China is not without its man-made scars. She is never far from the brink of starvation, holding her own in fairer spots only because of the utmost economy, hard toil, and huge reserves beneath her soil as well as beyond her immediate boundaries. And China is a nation in which prudent land management has been an official policy since 2700 B.C., the reign of the Emperor Shen-nung.

So much for China. What of India, whose teeming millions flit past the occidental imagination in a kaleidoscopic mixture of splendor and wretchedness? In montage we may see heaps of jewels, plump elephants, forests of precious woods, groves of spice and tea, rich fields of cane and rice. But always there are flashes of hungry faces, ragged bodies, crowding beggars, and all that symbolizes misery. No matter how many rotund and prosperous Indians one may have met face to face, the inescapable image of India to most Western minds is that of a gaunt and hopeless human figure, standing on sunbaked, barren clay beside an undernourished, wizened cow. Lest this seem too gross a caricature, let an Indian, the Agha Khan, speak:

"The ill-clad villagers, men, women and children, thin and weakly, and made old beyond their years by a life of underfeeding and overwork, have been astir before daybreak, and have partaken of a scanty meal consisting of some kind or other of cold porridge of course without sugar or milk. With bare and hardened feet they reach their fields and immediately begin to furrow the soil with their lean cattle of a poor and hybrid breed, usually sterile and milkless. A short rest at midday, and a handful of dried corn or beans for food, is followed by a continuance till dusk of the laborious scratching of the soil. Then the weary way homewards in the chilly evening, every member of the family shaking with malaria and fatigue. A drink of water, probably contaminated, the munching of a piece of hard black or green champatire, a little gossip round the peepul tree, then the day ends with heavy unrefreshing sleep, in dwellings so insanitary that no decent European farmer would house his cattle in them."

The specter of famine is never far away in India. It is estimated that in the famine of 1770 ten million died, amid scenes of suffering so harrowing that only a morbid mind would dwell upon them. So slight was the margin of supply that even three successive years of good crops thereafter could not restore the balance. Not enough people were left to work the fields. In 1865 one-third of the population of Orissa died by famine, and in the subsequent three years one and half million victims were claimed. The roster of Indian famines reads with an appalling monotony.

The Indian Empire is smaller than Greater China, but compares roughly with China proper in area and population. Northward the humid Gangetic plain and the arid Punjab are watered, as in China, by the huge Himalayas. Hence they are mostly covered by rich material washed over their surface. In the same sense as China, they are dependent upon treasures stored up in the past, as well as upon water and fertility brought today from the thinly populated Tibetan regions beyond their borders. They enjoy the added protection which comes from very moderate agricultural exploitation of their northern boundaries. Here considerable areas are occupied by tribesmen whose farming operations have been of a casual nature. More or less on the move, they have allowed their fields to grow back into forests after a few years of use—a custom which the climate permits. Thus the protecting girdle of vegetation is maintained from Tibet south into the hills of India. Should this be methodically stripped and the land put to the plow, it is easy to see that great skill would be required to prevent disaster to the more populous, lower valley regions.

The Dekkan, or peninsula of India, lying south of the regions named, is separated from them by a line of low mountains from which it receives the drainage. With the exception of its west coast, it is immediately dependent upon the rainfall, yet supports a dense population. The soil is peculiarly subject to erosion, and this evil has been intensified by removal of the forest cover from the hills which form the watersheds. Modern industrialism has encouraged and hastened this process. While the soil is varied, the direct cause of famines has been largely a recurring lack of rainfall. Soil management has not been on a level with that in China. Until recently fertility seems to have been maintained by a process of growing very little more than was needed to sustain life, and consuming it locally. In the absence of means of ready transportation even a local crop failure could produce starvation, and often did just that. Today, although British rule has alleviated conditions and permitted a vast increase in population, there is still hunger in case of local crop failures. Food in ample quantities can be brought in, but no one has the means to pay for it when it comes. Furthermore, the very railroads which facilitate the transportation of food have hastened the clearing of the forests which had earlier helped to check erosion.

Great Britain has not been indifferent to the problem of soil management and food production in India. In the drier parts there had already been a thrifty, well-managed irrigation economy, which she has undertaken to encourage. British agricultural experts are convinced that India can, under proper agricultural management, raise much more than sufficient for her own needs. But in the same breath they talk seriously about maintaining the soil in good condition if that is done. Production cannot be speeded up without recourse to artificial fertilizers and newer methods to which the population is not trained. The cattle of India are largely of inferior stock and undernourished because of food shortage during the dry season. In many places so great is the pressure for fuel that dung is gathered for that purpose, and so is not returned to the soil as it should be. In the newly opened irrigated regions where water is now abundant and the soil naturally good, increasing care will be required to keep the latter in proper condition in the face of oft-repeated waterings.

As to India, then, there is no warrant for talking of a really self-sustaining community. The richer parts are so because of what they receive from beyond their own borders. As to the rest, the price of survival has been a state of suspended animation for the whole populace, low vitality, and the constant threat of hunger. What has the upper hand here, man or nature?

But let us move on towards Egypt, that half-oriental teacher of the Western world. For practical purposes Egypt consists of a narrow thread of farm land along the lower Nile, widening into a delta as the mouth is approached. On her eight million acres are supported about ten million people. That is a population twice as dense as the most populous provinces of China or India. Her people are mostly hard-working, placid, peasant farmers, little concerned about sweetness and light, or the higher life. They use primitive tools, and methods that are age-old. In addition to the staples of ancient days, they now produce an excellent grade of cotton, in increasing amounts since the American Civil War. Heretofore there has been for them little trouble about keeping their soil fertile. The annual bath of mud, administered with gentle dignity by the stately Nile, has taken care of that. Along with the mud came water which could be impounded and fed out as needed by means of reservoirs in the upper part of the valley. In the delta, however, where there are no high levels in which to store water, only one crop could be grown, while the soil was still moist from the flood. Knowing that the climate would permit crops at any time of year, if only water were available, the authorities, in true modern high-pressure style, worked out a plan of ditches through the delta, to hold water in storage. By this means three crops a year could be grown, and the ground kept constantly at work. Great stuff!

Too good to last, in fact. The ditches kept the flood from anointing the fields with mud as usual, and soon the soil of the delta of the great river Nile, richest in the world, began to show symptoms very much like those of a broken-down, one-crop cotton or tobacco farm. It is clear now that if this soil is forced, it will exact compensation in the way of fertilizers.

And as to man's ever being self-contained and self-sustaining within the Nile Valley, not even the demagogues of old

Egypt would have dared preach that nonsense. The entire vast watershed of the river renders its tribute of water and topsoil to keep Egypt alive. In all the world today there is no better example of adroit, peaceful, absolute control of one nation over another than Great Britain exerts over Egypt by her possession of the Sudan, through which the river flows on its way to Egypt. She can throttle down the lower country to any degree she wills by withdrawing water to irrigate her own land. When a British high official was murdered in Cairo by a political assassin, the injured power countered by increasing the area of land under cultivation in the Sudan. For years Great Britain has been devoting some of her best scientific skill to thorough study of agricultural possibilities in the Sudan. Whether this has been primarily with a view towards producing more cotton and other raw materials, or to keep the Egyptians in a properly thoughtful frame of mind, is a topic upon which we need not expect His Majesty's government to be garrulous. Either way you take it you have a triumph of statecraft.

Outside of Egypt, what of the rest of northern Africa? The seacoast, once a famous wine district, is now unfit for that purpose. Egypt herself, beyond the immediate borders of the Nile, is desert. Both north and south of the Sudan is every evidence of misuse and deterioration—ground cover gone, soil washed and blown. In East Africa the pastures have been so overloaded with stock that here too the soil has been exposed and washed away. A curious exception occurs in places where the infestation of the accursed tsetse fly has kept down the cattle population. This pest, which has been a source of so much loss and destruction to the cattle industry, actually appears as a blessing when the long-time welfare of the continent is considered. It reminds us of the potato blight in western China, destroying food, it is true, but preventing destructive agriculture which would damage the watersheds supplying the populous districts near the coast. Again, it is like the boll weevil in the southern states, which, by ruining the cotton crop, finally forces the farmers to diversify their crops, to their own lasting benefit. Or like the wild hill people who occupy the northern reaches of India with their casual, precarious agriculture—insufficient to give them more than a meager living, but allowing the forest to keep its foothold so that the main part of India does not suffer as it otherwise would.

There is not much in the story of China, India, and Egypt to suggest that an entire continent can be exploited with the efficiency of the machine age, while its inhabitants multiply and enjoy what the politicians speak of as the "American standard of living."

One of the oldest Greek books we know about is a farm almanac. It is a good one, too, the *Works and Days* of Hesiod, dating probably from the eighth century B.C. It is addressed to a public of respectable small farmers, living on their own land and carrying on with the help of one or two slaves. Even today its precepts would be rated as sound and sensible. The course of time is measured by the stars, by the arrival of the swallow, or the fall of the leaf. "Mark, when you hear the voice of the crane who cries year by year from the clouds above, for she gives the signal for plowing and shows the season of rainy winter; but she vexes the heart of the man who has no oxen. . . . . When Zeus has finished sixty wintry days after the solstice, then the star Arcturus leaves the holy stream of Ocean and first rises brilliant at dusk. After him the shrilly wailing daughter of Pandion, the swallow, appears to men when spring is just beginning. Before she comes, prune the vines, for it is best so. But when the House-carrier [snail] climbs up the plants from the earth to escape the Pleiades, then it is no longer the season for digging vineyards, but to whet your sickles and rouse up your slaves. . . . when the artichoke flowers, and the chirping grasshopper sits in a tree and pours down his shrill song continually from under his wings in the season of wearisome heat, then goats are plumpest and wine sweetest. . . ." Not so precise as our printed calendars, but more to the point and in that sense more accurate. The old farmer of today who starts hunting the delicious morel mushroom when the apple trees burst into bloom comes back with a full basket oftener than his methodical city friend who has noted the date of April 1 for his foray. From Hesiod we get the picture of a Greek farming life that provides its own necessities and to spare, and of countrymen not ashamed of their task.

But as the centuries wore on—not many centuries, either—the owners left the land and others worked it. Steadily the lot of the actual farmer became worse, and the handling of the land less skillful. Presently the landlord was only concerned with the money rent he could get, and the tenant with what he could squeeze out of the soil with the forced labor of his slaves. The holdings became larger, too, as time went on, for the little individual owners could not compete with the larger landlords, and so gave up the struggle. In the end, of course, Athens became dependent upon shipments of grain from the people who lived in the lands beyond the Dardanelles, and when her enemies shut off the supply by sea she was lost. The failure of Greece is a complex tragedy of brilliant, undisciplined selfishness; and caught in the pattern is a tragic story of agricultural decline.

The modern Italian is one of the best farmers the world has ever seen. He can move in upon an abandoned New England stone pile and make it pay, and has done so to a considerable extent during the past few decades. One of the greatest agricultural treatises in history was that of Cato, if we except the lost writings of Mago the Carthaginian. It is illuminating to go through a good translation of Cato; we have one by the president of a southern railway, who signs himself "A Virginia Farmer." On every hand one finds practices recommended whose reason could not have been known to Cato, but which are sound from the point of view of modern science.

The Rome for which Cato wrote had been a land of sturdy yeomen who knew the soil and were not ashamed to manage their farms in person. But the course of farm life and farm management in Rome ran from yeomanry to tenantry, and finally to huge holdings of absentee landlords, worked by slaves under a supervisor. Augustus saw the danger of the decay of rural life and two great poets of his day lauded the farmer's simple career, Horace probably because he loved it, Virgil perhaps as an official task. In spite of the exceedingly fertile lands of northern Italy, watered and nourished from the Alps, Rome entered upon a period of agricultural decline and could not feed her own people. Neither Rome nor Greece succeeded in the conquest of nature, but it is true that neither tried with the persistence we have seen in oriental lands.

Elsewhere around the Mediterranean there is abundant evidence of decline. The situation in North Africa has already been described. Much of it which is now desolate was once reasonably fertile. Poor management, the ravages of war, and severe grazing by goats have broken whatever power the original soil had to temper the effects of the climate. In Spain the Moors were excellent farmers and handled the land well during the time of their enlightened civilization, which has been so fitly described as being "too finely perfumed to last." In regard to what happened after the Spaniards drove out the Moors we have to make ample allowance for the general lack of sympathetic insight into Spanish culture and history which has so long prevailed in the English-speaking world. Even so it seems true that agriculture suffered a backset when the Moors left. Doubtless in both Spain and southern France a good deal of the farming wisdom of the Romans persisted for a long time. There is certainly more evidence of its persistent effect there than in Britain. The terraced vineyards and olive groves of the south are works of perfection, yet they grow on land which the Norman lords probably would have considered fit only for wild game.

North of the Mediterranean the story of land management is confused by the presence of many small states, each with a complicated course of change in the system of land tenure and farm labor. Nearly everywhere, however, with increasing wealth and organization, the holdings became larger and the status of the actual worker worse. The manufacture of steel required charcoal in huge amounts, and the forests were early cleared to provide wood for the charcoal burners. This took place before the land was needed for agriculture, and long before the demand for lumber itself would have caused the cutting. The use of coal and coke in metallurgy is of course a very recent practice.

By the time of Charlemagne, who was an enlightened ruler, the onslaught against the forests of western Europe was under way, to continue through the thirteenth century. By the end of the Middle Ages the land was largely divested of its trees, as the Mediterranean region had been before the Christian era, and stringent laws against cutting came into being. Whatever advanced ideas had been inherited from Rome were soon lost to sight. Fields were used, then abandoned. Feudal lords shifted their headquarters from one castle to another, to get away, it has been said, from the accumulated filth. But the coefficient of toleration for filth was so high in those days that the moving was more likely to have been for the purpose of tapping new sources of food as the old sections of the fief played out. Eventually, after a period of rest, the abandoned fields had to be used again. Such a system is unsound. Recuperation takes too long, and too much of the land at a time remains idle. Paintings and sculptured figures of the period portray human beings who are wan and rickety, and since these portrayals were commonest in sacred art, most of us still have the feeling that anæmia and sainthood are inseparable. Actually the trouble was due to inadequate diet and malnutrition on a huge scale, such as we find in backward rural communities.

In contrast to the great landed estates, church property seems to have been well managed. As to the monks, even their friends are obliged to admit that they were well fed. In modern England the sites of old monastery gardens are still marked by little patches of savory plants, and such curiosities as the fat-leaved houseleek, or hen-and-chickens, which the good monks used to grow and pickle for winter use. To what extent the land-wise thrift of the church was due to its discipline and abundant resources, and to what extent to a knowledge of Roman agricultural lore it would be interesting to know. But to revile the monasteries for the benefit they received by keeping alive the tradition of good farming is as unjust as to censure the enlightened farmer of modern days for prospering when his careless neighbors fail. In either case the slow effect of example is the surest road toward the common good.

The stripping of the forests which has been mentioned not only produced a shortage of timber and fuel, but had other disturbing consequences, such as puddling of the soil and formation of acid heaths, particularly near the Atlantic. The result of this was to force upon Europe the early development of public and private forest policies—a scheme which incidentally fitted the idea of great royal and manorial hunting preserves.

In western Europe the re-introduction of sound land management came by degrees. As a first step the abandoned fields were kept clear of weeds, that is, kept in fallow. Later it was realized that crops should be rotated, for the effect of constantly growing the same crop on the same ground is mostly bad. The Romans had realized the value of including a legume, such as beans or clover, at some point in the rotation. Does not Virgil in his *Georgics* counsel the husbandman to "sow golden spelt, where before thou hadst reaped the pea with wealth of rattling pods, or the tiny vetch crop, or the brittle stalks and rustling underwood of the bitter lupin"? But the first rotations in western Europe did not include the legumes. Their regular culture came about slowly.

One of the earliest centers of diffusion for modern, effective farming in western Europe was the Netherlands, both Flemish and Dutch. It is an old axiom of agricultural history that the greatest progress comes where man has to be diligent in order to survive. The intensive skill required to reclaim and handle the lowlands proved to be as great a stimulus as irrigation had been in other parts of the world. The result was that with the Renaissance of the spirit throughout the Western world, there was a renaissance of sound land management in this area. Not only were legumes regularly included, but rotation systems which employed root crops were worked out, with immense benefit to man, beast, and land. These practices were not substantially improved until the day of modern, scientific, intensive rotation.

The awakening interest in science—"natural philosophy" —helped spread these ideas, and caused a search to be made for laws and explanations. The Dutch and Flemish taught their neighbors how to farm. This happy service came at a time when expanding populations taxed the existing food supply. Interest was further stimulated by the introduction of curious and valuable plants from the New World. Sometimes these plants reached western Europe in roundabout fashion. The French still call maize or Indian corn by the name *blé de Turquie*, or Turkish wheat, and of course the domestic turkey itself is an American bird. The word *potato*, now applied to a South American plant, is due to a confusion with the West Indian *batata*, our yam; while the prefix *Irish* has nothing to do with the real origin of the plant. Incidentally, the potato is an important illustration of the rôle which fashion played in the revival of agricultural practice in Europe. Statesmen realized the importance of this plant as a source of cheap and needed food for the poorer classes, but were obliged to use great ingenuity to break the chains of prejudice against its use. The Grand Monarque wore a sprig of potato blossoms at his lapel, and served the tubers at a stately banquet. Another enterprising gentleman guarded his patch against theft with ostentatious care until the crop was ready to dig. He then relaxed the guard and human nature took the next step, permanently inoculating the surrounding peasantry with a taste for this habit-forming vegetable.

Under Charles the Second, the seal of fashion's approval was set upon scientific experiment by the founding of the Royal Society of London. Slowly an understanding of the relation between soil, water, sunshine, and plant life developed. Modern chemistry, which had its beginning about the time of the American Revolution, helped the cause along immeasurably. The energetic German, Baron von Liebig, about one hundred years ago began his search for the perfect fertilizer, which would be applied artificially and forever do away with the problem of exhausted soils. Like the philosopher's stone and the elixir of life which the alchemists had sought, his dream was never to be realized in an absolute sense; but from his efforts came a better knowledge of both plant and soil. The great agricultural experiment station at Rothamstead, in England, was founded about 1843 as a private enterprise by Sir John Lawes, with the help of the scientist Gilbert, and its fields have been under continuous experimental control ever since.

Louis Pasteur's investigation of bacteria and other forms of microscopic life opened up new vistas of knowledge regarding the soil and its processes. Modern physics was drawn upon to explain many things that had been mysterious about the relation of water and soil. The ancient custom of legume rotation was proved to be a means by which nitrogen from the air was fixed in the soil through the work of bacteria growing on the roots of clovers and beans, and the practice justified as the cheapest, readiest means to supply this needed chemical substance. In dark, immense old Russia, whose little handful of scientists has at times seemed gifted with an eerie second sight, great things were done. The development of the soil itself was explained and shown to be, not a matter of years or generations, but of centuries, perhaps millennia. Soil is now known to be, not a substance, or a mixture of useful chemicals, but a phenomenon of the utmost complexity, whose delicate balance is easily disturbed and whose complete interpretation is yet far off.

The meaning of all these discoveries in a few words is this: The inexorable laws of cause and effect operate in the production of food from the soil just as in every other realm of physical experience. No man, no nation, can spend resources faster than they are built and escape the inevitable reckoning. It is impossible here, as elsewhere, to get something for nothing, and supreme folly to trust to the future for our errors to right themselves.

Meanwhile, what of the balance between man and nature in western Europe? Has this enlightened region been able to feed itself, and show a net gain? Since the great expansion of population with the introduction of steam and modern machinery, the area has not been able to supply itself with staple food. Instead of her farms, Great Britain has to depend upon her navy to keep the food channels to distant lands open. She rules the waves because it would be suicide not to do so. The French, because of their restricted rate of population increase, can perhaps come nearer being self-sustaining than their neighbors. But even they were starved out by the British navy during the Napoleonic wars—a circumstance which in the beginning caused Bonaparte to insist on developing the beet as a source of sugar to replace that from the tropical sugar cane.

Along with the French the smaller countries of western Europe, such as Holland and the Scandinavian lands, are restricting their population increase. Since 1922 England has been doing the same. The publication shortly before that of a book on contraceptive methods, and the open sale of this book, have had profound effect on the birth rate. It now appears, although such predictions are hazardous, that the population of England reached its maximum, at around thirty-nine million in 1938, and hereafter will decline steadily to about thirty-three million in 1976. All of the countries mentioned have, by government policy, private enterprise, and farmers' co-operatives, bent every effort to place their agriculture on a scientific basis. So far as possible, each is determined to supply its own needs. The soil is conserved, crops are rotated, and the best possible cultural methods employed.

But the fact remains that reserves in the form of chemical fertilizer must continually be added to the soil to maintain its productiveness. Bones from the battlefield of Waterloo, guano from the bird islands of the South Seas, phosphates from the United States, and nitrogen fixed by electricity from the air, have all poured onto the farms of western Europe in increasing amounts to replace the material taken out. The next step is inevitably the same careful use of human excrement which the Orient has had to practice, and already important experiments on the use of sludge from the great sewage disposal plants are under way. Ordinarily the residue from treated sewage is waxy in character and injurious to soil texture; but at least two great middle western municipalities have overcome this difficulty and are now producing excellent fertilizer from material which is generally wasted. The produce of their disposal plants not only contains nutrient minerals, but has the physical properties of ground peat or well-decayed leaf-mold which are so beneficent to soil.

It is essential to maintain a supply of the proper chemical elements in soil. It is quite as necessary to safeguard the texture of soil and to maintain its integrity as a biological milieu. This is the high test of husbandry. The wheat farmer who burns his stubble denies himself the services of bacteria which feed upon organic residues and, so doing, incorporate these residues into the soil. The landlord who, in regions of clay, clears away forests and fails to replace the decaying roots with plant and animal remains, will soon have tight and stubborn fields.

Poor Richard, Poor Lo

"The only good Indian is a dead Indian." It did not take the children of the Pilgrim fathers long to forget that the colony which landed at Plymouth Rock had been kept from starvation by friendly Indian help and tutelage in the art of New World agriculture. Old Squanto as an individual might be accorded the honor of perennial mention in history books, but the cultural and industrial achievements of his people were methodically omitted or else cruelly distorted. Thus the same generations which were nourished on the *Book of Martyrs*, and steeped in pity for white men who died for what they loved, found no difficulties excepting those of a technical character in crushing the red man and his works. And when, after about six generations, all Indians were evicted from the beautiful rolling lands of northern Ohio, the substantial citizen who ambushed a lonely stray and shot him in cold blood received little more censure than if he had killed a coyote. Between the English and the Indian it was war without quarter, almost from the start, with the end inevitable.

The reason is not far to seek. With that same granitic serenity wherewith the modern Briton transplants his tub, his cricket, and his teapot, the first Yankees were bent upon moving their British world along into the New World with them. And in particular, they brought their women, joined in lawful wedlock, thus introducing the fateful factor of competitive breeding. Not only did this intensify all the effects of invasion and conquest, but it provided a certain sanction for every aggressive move against the aborigines. One of the most significant traits of Anglo-Saxon psychology is the need for lofty motives during the process of getting whatever may be wanted. More a capacity for self-deception than a matter of perfidy or hypocrisy, it nevertheless lies at the root of much of the mischief done to the resources of the North American continent.

True it is, the clear-headed Latins came west with their own sanctions, extended by the Holy Church. And while these did not suffice to prevent cruelty and greed, there was this beautiful element of consistency: a race which was good enough to furnish converts was good enough for intermarriage. Undoubtedly this process of amalgamation was the easier because so many of the Romance invaders came as soldiers and traders. At any rate, where they settled the Indian and a great deal of his culture have survived.

The Englishman regarded with disfavor the Indian custom of allotting the agricultural labor to the woman, and pictured her as a slave. The fact is that she was not only at least as good a farmer as the average early English settler, but was happy in her work. The brave for his part had the responsibilities of war and chase. The fact that he was exterminated rather than enslaved carries its own comment on his character. It would be an interesting digression to compare the lot of the Indian woman with that of the white wife who was brought along on the first dark ventures into unknown perils and hazards. Yet it must be conceded that if the latter suffered, her daughters have come into their own. They now have title to about 70 per cent of the property in the United States, as well as preponderant influence in many cultural activities which their men have been too preoccupied to attend seriously.

The Indian culture which the Englishman destroyed along with its creators was diverse. In some respects it was on a level with that of his own Stone Age ancestors, in others far above. Of necessity it was in balance with nature, since the Indian had to adjust himself to nature rather than compel her. The Indian had a very keen sense of his dependence upon nature, and an aversion to needless waste of her resources, a fact which some of his sentimental friends like to dwell upon. But with his technical limitations it could not be otherwise. The mound builders whose elaborate and interesting works are found in Iowa, Wisconsin, and Ohio, represent a comparatively high type of culture which at one time spread out to the limits named from some southwestern center. However they could not maintain existence in the face of difficulties, probably caused by the encroaching forest with its marauding groups of hunters. As a result they had been driven back before the whites arrived. Their technical control of the environment was too slight to succeed permanently in peaceful farming villages and they vanished. Given steel tools for work and war, domestic animals to labor and furnish food, the tale might have ended differently. It is well to remember that the Indian had cultivated all of the New World plants which have been found to be worth the trouble, and had excellent methods for doing so.

A feature of the Indian's close relation to nature was his lack of any sense of private property in land. The land was there to be used and the general right to its use had to be determined, on occasion, by bloodshed. But its use was for the subsistence of the group, not for private gain. In this sense it has been well said that in the Indian land agreements with the white, the red man sold one thing, the white bought a very different.

To the Englishman, on the other hand, the right of a commoner to private ownership of real estate was a serious matter, the fruit of centuries of struggle against a powerful social and economic system. Not only was his house his castle, but his lands were his to use, enjoy, exploit, or ruin, as he would. The only checks were the requirement that he pay taxes levied by his own lawful representatives, and the provision of escheat, or return of the land to the government in case its owner died with no heirs.

The first settlers in New England were largely townspeople, not skilled in the art of farming. Even had they been mostly country born, it probably would have made little difference. British agriculture of the day had not yet learned its lessons from the efficient lowlanders. It involved problems of soils, crops, and climate more or less different from those encountered by the settlers, and was organized on a manorial basis for which there was no use in New England. On the other hand the settlers were ingenious craftsmen, industrious, thrifty, and determined. Had they been without these qualities, they could not have survived. They spread out over the land, it is true, and made their own subsistence from the thin, rocky soil. But their real energy went into manufacturing, marine enterprise, and business, ending of course in the severe, direct, commercial rivalry with the mother country which brought on the Revolution.

South of New England, in New York and Pennsylvania, there was a larger proportion of good farming land, much of which was settled by Germans, Dutch, and Swedes. More than in the English, there was ingrained in these people a sense of good farm management. Their practices soon became, and still remain, models of their kind. Their farms were beautifully kept. Fortunately the growing cities of the seacoast afforded a ready market, permitting money to be used in maintaining fertility. If conditions everywhere were like those of the fruit, truck, and dairy regions of eastern Pennsylvania and central New York, there would be no deserts on the march today.

Scarcely had the Revolutionary War ended when surveyors, and after them settlers, began moving into the country north and west of the upper Ohio River. By 1800 the movement was well under way. All elements of the colonial population save perhaps the great southern manorial owners took part, although even the latter were involved as capitalists. Increasing numbers of emigrants from Europe swelled the tide. The only challenge that was apparent was that of occupying the land. Water-mill sites were prized locations.

Occasional open glades interrupted the dense hardwood forests, becoming larger and more frequent from Ohio westward, until they expanded into the vast domain of the prairie. These natural grasslands were not immediately utilized. Instead the settlers chose the forest. The prairies with their richer soil were at first used only for pasture, coming very gradually under cultivation, particularly as tile drainage was adopted.

The forest itself, although a welcome source of fuel and timber, as well as game, was regarded principally as an obstacle to agriculture. Not only was wood used lavishly, but the felled logs of valuable, even precious wood, were rolled into huge piles and burned. Walnut and wild cherry fed the flames along with elm and cottonwood. Perhaps this was inevitable, but it is worth noting that the field books of the first surveyors contain abundant evidence that they knew the value of the forests through which they worked. So far as anyone can determine, these records were never utilized in any respect for public good save as that end might be served through the foresight of the individual settler or the speculator who followed in his wake. When we recall that the center of the commercial lumbering activities did not move west of New York until after 1850 it is easier to understand the apathy of the early nineteenth century towards forest conservation. Not only great sagacity, but a greater immunity to political pressure than our statesmen commonly show would have been required to establish the reserves or restrictions which we now know should have been made for the common good. And it may be doubted whether such precautions would have been worth the trouble, in view of the squatters and other lawless gentry which abounded. It is no secret that the government has not yet won the Whisky Rebellion which started in Washington's administration.

Other circumstances were unfavorable to what we might call a psychology of permanence. In the beginning the urgent need was to meet each day's practical problems as they arose without worrying much about the future. Later the processes of urbanization and industrial change occurred so rapidly as to be bewildering. It took a strong character or an utter lack of enterprise to avoid riding the tide for profit's sake. To a degree even the best citizens conducted themselves like the shell-game man at the county fair, on the basis of quick action. Yet it is only just to note that many monuments to the future in the way of schools and other humane institutions had their origin in this period.

The resourcefulness of the early rural population was remarkable. The farms of that day were self-supporting to an extent undreamed of now. Home-grown wool and flax were spun and woven at home, and there made into clothing. Light came from homemade candles, cast from beef and mutton tallow. These had their faults, as anyone who has inhaled the aroma from incandescent mutton fat will know. But they cost no cash outlay. The tiny driblets of cash which a modern family would despise were hoarded, often to be used in the purchase of additional land. Many a family which had struggled through years of toil and painful saving found itself at last wealthy, for the value of land steadily increased as population developed. Good business management was held in high social esteem, but there was no corresponding pressure to encourage wise husbandry of the land. Land was land, to be mined until it could be sold for a profit.

The professional classes were on the whole an excellent group. Generally prosperous and often public spirited, they were at once an influence for stability and unrest. The example they afforded did much to drain the farms of their ablest young men. The unremitting toil and lack of conveniences, let alone luxuries, which the farm implied were constant incentives to escape. Added to this must be the temption to retire to town or village which assailed farmers and their families who had continued the struggle long enough to become wealthy. Seldom indeed was this sort of translocation successful, as the old proverb, "one generation between shirt-sleeves and shirt-sleeves," witnesses.

Despite the rapid industrial progress, there set in a serious decay of rural life. The land, already exploited rather than conserved, was turned over to tenants, generally without the protection of just and intelligent contract, and in half a century the vicious cycle which, spreading over centuries, had ruined Greece and Rome, was on its way. The tenants, like their owners, lacked the steadying effect of a long agricultural tradition. Such apprenticeship as they had was in what was, at best, a predatory type of farming. Thus it happened, that while people in the Middle West were discussing the tragedy of abandoned farms in New England, their own land was moving rapidly toward the same fate.

We have seen that the center of lumbering lay in western New York as late as 1850. Thence it shifted to Ohio and Indiana, and then quickly into Michigan, Wisconsin, Minnesota, and since has shifted to the Gulf and Pacific coasts. In every instance until recently the method was that of clean cutting, with no thought of permanent yield. This policy was applied with equal vigor on land which had farming possibilities and that which had none. Rather generally the best potential farm land was occupied by farmers before clearing, and the lumber sold from it by them. The great holdings of land suitable only for forest were stripped by the companies in control, after which attempts were made to colonize farmers on them, often with sorry consequences.

Following on the heels of the main lumbering activity were numerous industries which utilized second-growth timber and remnants. Stave and hoop mills, bending works, wagon and handle factories, may be mentioned among these transient industries which shifted west in a slow afterwave. They represent merely one of the many proofs of instability. The psychology was not one of a settled order. People never felt that they must face their immediate surroundings with any finality, even though they might have passed most of their days in one spot. If things became too bad, moving was always possible, and land elsewhere was still cheap. In consequence the obligation to conserve the soil was scarcely felt, and the farm itself came, as we have seen, to be regarded as a mere stepping stone into the professional or commercial life of the rapidly growing towns.

Meanwhile the developments of commerce, fuel, ore, and manufacture, and the sequence of wars, booms, and panics in the Middle West served to obscure the serious character of the agricultural tragedy that was being enacted. "Our Uncle Sam is rich enough to give us each a farm," ran the old song. The retired Ohio farmer could take his profits and put them into cheap land in Iowa. True, there were no railroads in northwestern Iowa, but after the land was acquired, a word with an old friend in the United States Senate—all perfectly honorable—and the branch road sprouted out in the proper direction, to the good of everybody concerned.

Probably Iowa deserves as much credit as any state for arresting the blind progress of pillage. There are older experiment stations and agricultural colleges than hers, perhaps even better ones. But nowhere before had such institutions enjoyed such public confidence and been so concrete a factor in the state's policy as in Iowa. Here at last was a state in which agriculture was not merely one ring, but the whole circus. The result was that Iowa land was well managed and commanded a continuously high price, even after much of it, too, was actually handled by tenant farmers. Beyond question this was largely due to the influx of Norwegians and other Scandinavian farmers experienced in the skillful and careful husbandry of their perfectly managed European farmsteads.

Farming in Iowa, and in the parts of Kansas, Nebraska, Minnesota, and the Dakotas known as the grain belt, enjoyed a definite status. Instead of a makeshift, or an outcast occupation, it was regarded as a prospering, well-managed enterprise. This position was not won without a period of false starts and discouragements which eliminated all but the most successful and persistent, especially west of the Missouri River. In Wisconsin the portions suitable for dairying became specialized for that industry and still occupy a premier position. In the cut-over forest land of the northern lake states, however, attempts, often strongly sponsored by the exploiters, to convert such land into farms were largely unsuccessful. In the end, they proved very costly, not only to the individual colonizers who failed there, but to the eventual profitable reforestation of that region. It is worthy of note that the ultimate failure of these schemes was predicted by competent agriculturists. At least one such man was forbidden to make public statements about the matter.

It would be an error to say that the soil of the grain belt farms maintained its fertility undiminished. But it has been, on the whole, well managed. Timber claims were started in many places, somewhat tempering the individual homesteads and fields against wind and sun. The worst error of management has been the failure to keep an adequate reserve of land unplowed as pasture or hay meadow. Most farmers of the grain belt would today be better off than they are with perhaps a fourth of their land in productive pasture—to provide them with their own milk and beef, if nothing more, while hedging the risk to soil and water supply on fields that are tilled.

In the second place, the pattern of farm finance which developed in the grain belt was thoroughly vicious and against the public interest. This is not to say that any individual responsibility can be fixed. By the policy the banks profited hugely for many years at the expense of their own clients, but in the end the banks crashed with the rest of the system. The wrong of this system was the failure to appraise land on the basis of its average yield. This is a particularly serious matter in an area where the climatic margin of safety for good crops is never high, and where the rainfall fluctuates greatly. There are certain to be years of good crops and years of failure. In good years everyone who has some money saved wants to buy a farm. Under such conditions the banks permitted their customers to pay more for land than, on a sound average, it was worth. Inevitably came the years of crop failure. Payments could not be maintained, and the bank which had advanced the money—after receiving a large down payment—got back the land and of course retained the payment. It was not uncommon for a bank to resell the same piece of land four or five times, each time with a handsome profit at the expense of some client's life saving. The fisherman who has to use a fresh worm for each catch will appreciate the remarkable features of this system.

Of course land values ought to be computed on an actuarial basis, as life insurance premiums are, even though this task is the harder. But it would be a distinct improvement if banking ethics did not permit a customer to pay more for land than the banker himself would care to pay in order to receive adequate returns.

The northern farmer, then, moved across the continent with the complete destruction of native Indian culture, emphasizing at every step individual property rights in the land without regard for public policy. Until the grain belt states were reached and self-interest dictated better measures, the farming areas were systematically impoverished and the lands exhausted.

Within the grain belt, although a high level of soil management was inaugurated, too small a proportion of native grassland was retained as a reserve and safeguard against climatic fluctuations and soil removal. Further a system of farm finance developed which was essentially unsound, impoverishing the farm population and ultimately the financial institutions which served the area.

We have followed the European west through the northern states and into the eastern portion of the great interior grasslands. Before moving farther west into the short-grass plains, where much of our story lies, let us retrace our steps to the Atlantic coast and work westward once more, this time with a different breed of men, the southern colonists.

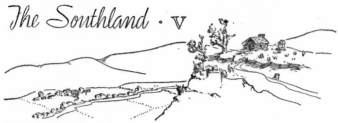

The Southland · V

Long before the whites moved west from the Atlantic coast, their pressure on the Indians had caused serious disturbances far inland. In particular the rich though rough and broken region which is now Kentucky and West Virginia had been depopulated and was serving as a no-man's land separating hostile tribes, with distinctive types of culture. The southern tribes, increasingly toward the Gulf, displayed a settled village economy, with highly developed agriculture. They possessed extensive earthworks, storehouses, various crafts, and commerce. Plainly they showed signs of influence radiating not only from Mexico, but from the Antilles, and because of the genial climate, they possessed a rich variety of cultivated plants.

Curiously, the same dark and bloody ground which had separated the Indians was destined to cleave the white Europeans into two profoundly different cultures. North of it was the strongly individualistic middle class from the Old World, each member conscious of his own hard-won rights and the new freedom to exercise them in a region of unbounded resources. In these people considerable practical and mechanical sense was combined with the habit of hard work. Excepting for the Teutonic groups among them, they were not, as a rule, first-class farmers. We have seen the result, in a trail of impoverished land extending west to the grain belt, but accompanying it a brilliant record of commercial and industrial growth.

South of the dark and bloody ground, the picture grows more complex. Here the gentlefolk of old England were granted huge estates. With them as workers came the impoverished, the inefficient, and the failures from various levels of society. Black slaves, which soon proved unprofitable in the northern states, were found to be decidedly the reverse in this warmer region. Tobacco, cotton, indigo, and sugar cane could be grown in addition to staple food crops, and were as readily convertible into cash as the products of the northern industries. And like the factory products it was soon discovered that they could be most profitably and economcially produced on an extensive scale. Just as in the North the small independent shop was to give way to the large, centrally managed factory, so in the South the small, personally owned and worked farm could not compete with the large, efficiently managed plantation.

Along with this circumstance was another, destined to cost a staggering total in the ensuing centuries. The wealthy controlling group classed education along with the other good things of life—a luxury to be dispensed only to those who had the price to pay for it. There is no use at this late date to chide them. This position seemed as logical and just to them as some of the pinheaded policies of the Northerners seemed to the latter. The poorer class of whites, driven out of owning the richest lands by competition, and kept from employment on these lands by black labor, were also kept in ignorance. Furthermore, since the mechanical duties in connection with the larger plantations were cleverly performed by trained blacks, there was little opportunity for the whites to become, through apprenticeship, skillful artisans like those of the North. In the end, the blight of ignorance rested not only upon the impoverished white misfits of the lower classes, but even upon the poorer kinsmen of the wealthy landowners.

The best land in the South lay along the coastal plain and in the rich broad valleys that ran inland from it. This of course came under the control of the great landlords. To survive, the poorer whites had literally to take to the hills. And while the seacoast, both along the Atlantic and the Gulf, became a region of wealth and culture, the interior developed its own discipline and its own significant character. The line of cleavage within the South was as distinct as the cleavage between North and South. Had the Civil War not intervened when it did, the South eventually might have witnessed a civil war of its own. For the people of the interior hills came to realize they had one weapon, the ballot, and by 1840 they were using it with telling effect. In Mississippi and Louisiana they forced the removal of the political capitals away from the coast, and into the interior.

Meanwhile, the Indians had been largely cleared out. Some few in the Carolinas managed to hang on, adopting the culture of the poor whites. Farther west, among the civilized tribes, the plantation system, with slaves and large holdings, was put into operation. But throughout the South, which with the exception of the factory region about Birmingham and the great shipping centers, was predominantly agricultural, the custody of the land fell into the hands of the white race. How was this trust discharged?

Despite their faults, the landed gentry had great virtues. Bright among these was the strong sense of public duty, even though it might not always extend to popular education. Under these circumstances, good land management and enlightened agriculture became a moral obligation as well as being good business. George Washington exemplifies this attribute, and often hidden behind his better known titles is that of "Father of American Agriculture." He was a notable student of the subject, diligent in the handling of his land, and concerned to introduce the best possible methods. Despite his example and his efforts, which were repeated through all of the plantation country, the fertility of the coastal plain and great valleys was steadily depleted, so that today their fertility can only be maintained by costly applications of fertilizer.

Perhaps this would have been unavoidable in any case. The soil layer is generally light, underlaid largely by sand. The constant demand for cash crops made it extremely profitable to grow the same crop repeatedly, even if the expense of fertilizer was necessary. Anyone who has watched the ash grow at the end of a burning cigar may realize how much material the tobacco plant takes from the soil. All of the ash, and not a little of the smoke, represents stuff drawn up from the soil.

But the main trouble with agriculture in Washington's time was the same thing that handicapped the medical practice which bled him to death in his last illness. Both were looking to science for light before science had the light to dispense. Under such conditions the most conservative position is the safest. In medicine the physicians of the Middle Ages had developed many practical measures which they could not explain, but which had the merit of working. For example, they burned fresh wounds with a hot iron. At the time of the French Revolution all of these old practices were cast aside as being superstitious. Medicine attempted to be scientific, with awful results. Instead of cauterizing fresh wounds, they were bandaged in lint, which we know must have been bacteriologically filthy. Gangrene was the usual consequence. In Washington's day the relation of soil, air, water, and sun to plant life was just beginning to be understood. Some of the aspects most important for agriculture were not discovered until a century later; and of course, there is still much to learn.

Had the coastal plain been farmed throughout by industrious peasants, drilled in the routine of the best agricultural tradition of Germany or Flanders, it is probable that it would have remained more productive than it did under its relatively ambitious management. The peasants would not have been able to explain the scientific basis for their practice, but the practice itself would have been sound. There is today in South Carolina an area which has long been occupied by Germans. All around it is desolation, caused by erosion. This erosion of course was induced by improper soil management. Within the area in question erosion is comparatively slight, although the physical character of the land is like that of the surrounding region.

Not all of the coastal plain was given over, of course, to plantations. Toward the south the extensive areas of longleaf pine yielded timber and naval stores, while the swamps contained valuable cypress and gum. It is almost unnecessary to remark that the development of these forest resources was, until very recently, a matter of exploitation rather than conservation. The situation was aggravated by fire, which in some cases apparently produced barren areas largely unfit for any use. The turpentine trees were tapped by boxing, which quickly destroyed their value, either for turpentine or timber, and made them an easy prey to the frequent burning.

Above the coastal plain lay the foothills and mountains. In some cases there were broad and fertile valleys, but oftener the fertile valley land lay in narrow isolated strips. Hither the poorer white population was forced to retreat in order to survive. Hill and valley alike were wooded, with a rich variety of trees. To the settler, here as in the North, the forest was a hostile thing, occupying the ground which he needed for corn and beans, even though it furnished him with game, fuel and building material. All was fair in the struggle against this handicap, and no weapon, not even his sharp ax, was more powerful than fire. So the use of fire against the forest became a part of the ritual of the poor white. He has literally burned his way west, from the pinelands of the Carolinas to the blackjack cross timbers of Oklahoma and Texas.

The economy thereby introduced was one of clearing the forest by fire, farming the cleared place so long as it yielded well, repeating the process until it became necessary to move to a new location. This is Stone Age technique, of course. Practiced by the ancient Mayas, it defeated them. Practiced by the hill people of northern India, it keeps them on the move, and keeps down their population. And in western Europe it was long ago abandoned in favor of more permanent methods.

No less than the wealthy planter, the mountain white possessed his virtues along with his vices. A common error is to regard him as of inferior metal biologically. Of course, as may happen in any mountain region, for example Switzerland, there have been isolated districts in which inbreeding, combined with ignorance and disease, has produced genuine racial deterioration. But for many years it has been known that no finer soldiers are found in the United States army than those recruited from the hills. Given proper influences the young people develop into excellent, even distinguished citizens. Witness the thrifty young products of modern 4-H clubs, not to mention Lincoln and his successor. Anyone who has traveled among the mountain whites is familiar with their fine, instinctive courtesy and general decency. The fact that their women lead lives of hard work and wear out quickly is often misunderstood. Their women are held in high regard and the division of labor is a necessary one. These people are not fundamentally lawless. It is true that laws made and administered out of their sight have little force. But their own code is definite, and strictly enforced, even though the means used may be extralegal.

A young engineer from the North who has lived among them for a number of years says, "When I first saw how hard they worked and how little they had, I thought they were to be pitied. Now that I know them better I think they lead much happier lives than the rest of us. They are not lazy. Those whom you see sitting in front of their houses at midday were up before dawn and had done a good day's work. They are not dirty. I have eaten with them frequently, and often shared a one-room cabin with a family of six or seven at night. The children, even the older girls, undress without self-consciousness down to clean undergarments and retire, as do the boys and men. The mother usually waits to put out the light, then prepares for bed. They are fine, decent people."

When the depression struck, it caught them at first unprepared, as it did everyone else. But immediately they took steps to store up reserves from their excellent gardens and the abundant wild fruits about them, as well as their casually managed livestock. The second winter of the depression found them in tidy shape. True, there was government aid, and even a rumor or two that relief sugar, ostensibly for canning, was being converted into a more marketable product, but on the whole the mountain whites have weathered the storm. The very simplicity and self-contained character of their living made it possible to do this with the least possible adjustment. An anthropologist who visited them for the first time said, "I have found a neolithic culture. The metal tools and manufactured junk they have are only incidental, and merely emphasize the self-sufficient, primitive economy under which they live." Without any great taste for mechanical devices, they nevertheless possess an uncanny skill with simple tools. A cabin in the Cherry River district of West Virginia was built, fenced, neatly and conveniently furnished with saw and ax—mainly the latter.

So long as these people are not too densely settled, and the uplands about their valleys are richly wooded, they can maintain themselves. But if lumber companies clear the woods, or they themselves persist in burning them to improve pasture, or worst of all attempt to farm the hills, the end comes quickly. The hills erode and the small rich valley fields are buried under the waste. The southern hills are full of the skeletons of cabins.

From the most hopeless of the mountain whites and doubtless other sources comes the derelict white humanity of the South. Mill hands, itinerant cotton pickers, and forlorn tenant farmers are included here. They are in direct economic competition with the blacks. If not on the move, they are found as workers on neglected land, held by absentee speculators for one reason or another. Their plight has attracted enough attention in high places to spare its discussion here. They are not to be blamed if the land they occupy is skinned and ruined. Few are trained as farmers. Few have sufficient capital or income to manage well if they could. The owners of the land on which they live are more often than not purely predacious and the land generally is run down when they move on-to it. Their pastures are loaded to the limit. The timber is stripped off and hauled in to sell for fuel. Any land that promises even one or two good crops is likely to be cleared and plowed, regardless of the after effects. They have few milk cows and those inferior. There is a shortage of manure for the fields, and no money for commercial fertilizer. Frequently vitality is so lowered by disease, malnutrition, and bad heredity that it is hopeless to expect the energy which would be needed for good management, even if all other essentials were provided. In these human derelicts we see the cumulative effects of three centuries without popular education, social discipline, economic opportunity, or good craftsmanship.

As tenants they have been crowded off the well-managed farms of the South in favor of dependable blacks or enterprising whites. They are to be found on marginal and sub-marginal land, most of which in the East should be back in forest, in the West in grass. The zones they occupy can be selected from the air by the red or yellow gleam of sterile eroded hills. Although their hands may have hastened the destructive forces of nature, the responsibility to society is one which, in all justice, should not be laid to their charge.

Through the pine forests of the Gulf states and the oak forests of the Ozarks the white man debouched upon the southern part of the great interior grassland. Here, south of the grain belt, is a rolling terrain of varied soils and possibilities. Leased in great holdings of thousands of acres by the cattlemen, the coming of homesteaders was viewed by at least one of the latter with complacency. "They cannot farm this country and live," said he. But farm it they did. The valleys were rich and fertile. Even the uplands gave good crops at first—wheat, oats, corn, sorghum, and cotton.

The fire god was invoked to clear what woods there were and to improve the shrinking pastures. In the hands of the old cattleman fire had been used, if at all, with care and skill. Now it was brandished recklessly, destroying humus and killing valuable kinds of pasture plants. Pastures were overloaded. Upland fields were carelessly planted in row crops. In a few decades, save for the exceptional, well-managed holdings, the once green countryside showed everywhere the scar of soil destroyed, and even the rich valleys became nonproductive.

Once again we have reached the eastern portion of the great grassland, this time by the southern route. We have traveled from the fair valleys of Virginia, which even the foresight and care of Washington could not preserve from loss of fertility, to a region into which man has swept like a devouring plague, reducing much of it from a prosperous cattle country to a region of deserted and deteriorating farms, in four decades.

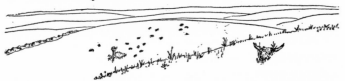

The short-grass and sagebrush country represent about the last stand of that legendary hero, the pioneer, unless one sees in the modern racketeer something more than is really there. Upon the cowpuncher fell the spiritual poncho of Adam Poe, Daniel Boone, and Kit Carson after these shadowy figures had passed to a still more shadowy beyond. From the days of the dime thriller to the "Western" his name has been bathed in glory—a source of constant inspiration and dependable profits. This being the case, exactly who were the cowmen?

Economically, they were hired hands, working for others. Personally, they ranged from the usual type of hired hand one finds anywhere, to charming and gifted exiles whose existence elsewhere had been fraught with disappointment. Frequently they had been the source, rather than the victims of this disappointment. It was essential that they ride horseback, and desirable that they develop sufficient skill and judgment to keep from getting their guts kicked or trampled out. Riding and even roping are more matters of practice than of divine inspiration. Beyond this the demigods of the range were kept in excellent physical condition by the kind of life they led. Their sense of proportion was kept in order by group discipline—a home-made sort of psychoanalysis known as "sandpapering the ego" or "applying the cactus." All told, they were a good lot, patrolling for their overlords a domain that reached west from the grain belt through the mountains, and extended from Canada to Mexico.

Their employers were enterprising capitalists, engaged in quantity production of beef and hides. By purchase or lease they enjoyed the grazing rights on vast areas. The grazing lands of a single owner might be together, but were frequently scattered, giving thus a better possibility of shifting the load with the seasonal and yearly changes in pasture and water supply. Necessarily they were in close touch with the breeding and feeding of their animated wealth, and understood the vital importance of conserving the range. The objects of resentment and envy from the land-hungry to the east of them, they labored under the added handicap of being unable to secure permanent control of much of the land which they used.

After 1870, with the development of transcontinental railroads and the systematic destruction of the buffalo, the livestock industry expanded with amazing rapidity through the plains area of the western states. There was no legitimate mechanism by which an individual owner could secure outright possession from the government of enough land to engage in this industry with any assurance of safety and profit. The homesteads, while large as compared with a typical eastern farm, were too small for a semiarid region. The huge grants made to the great railroads were not consolidated, but scattered. It was of course possible, but often difficult, for the wealthy operator to buy out a number of homesteaders and get the land he needed. If the land so purchased made a solid block, it was unusual.

The other recourse was to use the land of others, with or without rental. Gradually, therefore, a system of leased grazing rights developed throughout the entire western cattle country, resulting in serious, too often permanent, damage to the range. Here, as in the great lumbering operations of the same period, we see not a fair trial of a system of responsible private ownership, but the concession system operating in its worst form. Had it been possible to allot as permanent holdings sufficient areas to individual cattlemen, there is reason to think that the quality of the range might have been conserved. For the cattleman, unless he were a non-resident capitalist, differed in certain important respects from the lumber baron.

The latter, for example, had about the same interest in trees that the butcher might be expected to have in cattle. The trees were ready at hand. But it had not been necessary to supervise their breeding, birth, and growth, or to move them about to prevent their dying of hunger and thirst. So far as the lumberman was concerned, nature could grow new trees while he made off to fresh sources of supply.

On the other hand, the chief responsibility of the cattle industry was to grow the thing that was to be sold. This meant attention to sources of supply for food and water. The cattleman soon learned that a badly overloaded range meant inferior pasture in succeeding years. But since he so seldom had the title to his pasture, the temptation to make immediate profit while he could was too strong to resist. Resulting directly from this pattern of exploitation has been the periodic over-expansion of the cattle industry, more or less following on the intervals of heavier rainfall and more abundant grass. These events not only produced a surplus of cattle, ruining the market, but threw an abnormally heavy load on the range at the beginning of the several dry periods, furthering rapidly the ultimate destruction of the grassland turf. Under the system of land allotments, any planned and provident economy became well-nigh impossible.

In addition, the livestock industry was faced with other and serious problems. Sheep are as essential as cattle to modern civilization, particularly in cool, temperate regions where woolen clothing must be worn. Like goats, however, they are thin-lipped, sharp-biting animals capable of cropping very close to the ground. Their small hoofs are edged and will cut and wear the turf unless care is taken. On the English golf courses sheep are used as lawn-mowers. In that moist climate the grass grows rapidly and the animals keep it cropped to a close green velvet. If land in regions of high rainfall were not too valuable for sheep pasture, it would afford the best setting for that purpose. Actually, however, it generally becomes necessary to pasture great flocks of sheep in semiarid regions where the grasses have only a brief growing season, remaining the rest of the year dormant and dried—a sort of half-living hay—on the stalk. Under these conditions considerable care and expense is required to keep the flocks of sheep on the move and prevent lasting damage to the range. Moreover, there is a belief that cattle do not like to graze over ground that has been fed upon by sheep.

It can be appreciated then that the entrance of sheep into the cattle country meant the declaration of war. A mild and kindly ranchman who, like Cowper's friend, would not needlessly set foot upon a worm, describes without batting an eye how great flocks of sheep, coming too near his demesne, are inexplicably clubbed to death, or have their throats cut. Which suggests again the very practical attitude of the cattleman towards conservation of the range.

Towards the would-be small homesteader he could scarcely defend himself by such direct action, although no doubt the intimate history of the West might produce instances in which he did so. Against the settler his only defense could be, in the long run, previous personal ownership of all of the land which he used. The weakness of his position lay in the fact that he was obliged to count on leasing large areas of the public domain to continue in business. And towards this domain hungry eyes were cast.

Probably the great transcontinental railroads, which at first provided a welcome outlet for his cattle, but which also fostered colonization, were inevitable sources of trouble. Mining operations often enriched him. At the same time they helped build centers of population, creating customers, it is true, but also bringing in hordes of the land-hungry. In the end, it was pressure from this last group, encouraged as often as expressed by professional politicians, which caused the cattle industry to suffer most.

Yet in spite of difficulties, the livestock industry made substantial strides toward permanence. The periodic maladjustments wiped out the plungers and exploiters. The large operators who have survived are those who have been sufficiently farsighted and conservative to prevent their being caught by cycles of overproduction, and in particular those who have steadily used their profits to acquire title to their own ranges. At their best, such men have developed a sense of responsibility for the welfare of the humans, the animals, and the land under them comparing favorably with that of the finer type of great plantation owner in the old South. An additional factor which contributed to stabilize the industry was the recognition of priority lease rights to government land, and in particular, the enforcement of regulated grazing thereon. It is quite probable that if general conditions in the country at large could have remained economically balanced, the livestock industry might have shared in this general stability, and the region which supported it have developed an equilibrium. Such has not been the case. But before examining the latter end of the story, it is well to acquaint ourselves with a region whose history is as graphic as a diagram.

The Sand Hills of Nebraska contain about eleven million acres—an area larger than the agricultural portion of Egypt. It consists of billowing, grass-covered hills lying in a vast rock bowl which holds the meager rainfall and slowly passes it up through the loose sand. In summer, when the pastures east of it are parched and dry, the grass here is green and fresh. But here and there, as fateful warnings which spoke plainly to the practised eye, were great blowouts. These were funnel-shaped craters dug by the wind into the sand wherever the grass had been removed and the weak turf destroyed. Within these craters is a summertime inferno with temperatures often as high as one hundred and forty degrees, while even a moderate wind converts them into a withering, etching sand-blast. With all her resources, nature has a painful task to reclaim these blowouts. Given time, she can do it by means of the wiry creeping rootstocks of Redfield's grass, followed slowly by other venturesome plants, and ultimately by the original turf-forming grasses.

So long as this land remained in public domain, it was leased in large blocks and used as cattle range. Between the hills were numerous lakes where the underground water came to the surface, and about their shores were meadows of grass which could be cut and cured for winter feed. By the use of large areas for each individual operator, overloading of the pasture on the hilltops could have been prevented, as doubtless it frequently was, and the turf thus allowed to remain and hold the sand in place. But a kingdom like this, the size of Egypt, was too tempting to be allowed such use. It became a political issue. The Sand Hills should be carved up into homesteads, each one mile square, and given to the people. Finally a man was elected to Congress on the issue—Moses Kincaid. He secured the passage of the necessary homestead law, and the settlers who thronged in on these claims were known after him as "Kincaiders."

The Kincaiders often lacked sufficient capital, as well as previous experience with the difficulties which lay ahead of them. Most unfortunately, the area assigned to each homestead, one square mile, was too small to support a family under the conditions which prevailed there. Some confined their activities to cattle but were faced with the fact that enough cattle to support them made too heavy a load on the range. The close-cropped turf broke through, and the sand began to blow, spreading ruin. Others boldly attempted to plow the ground and plant crops. On the lowland there was some return for this trouble, but at the expense of the hay meadows. On the upland, the wind swept down and across the planted rows, swirling the sand into the leaves of the planted crop and shredding them to pieces, finally either burying the crop or uncovering its roots.

Easter week of 1920 a family of these homesteaders extended their hospitality to two foot-travelers, with a grace that would have adorned a more stately mansion than the tiny sod house. In the house was a little flour, a little coffee, a few potatoes, and happily, water with which to prepare all three.

No milk, no butter, no eggs, no meat. Not one sign was there that the guests might be making inroads on a scant provision— only regret that the repast was not more varied. These brave people were the lords of six hundred and forty acres—a space which in Egypt keeps alive one thousand—yet they were slowly starving. When the travelers took their leave, they were cheerfully urged to return in August to help eat watermelons because "that's sure one thing we kin grow in these valleys, melons."

As the discouraged and defeated Kincaiders retreated from the picture their homesteads were gradually acquired once more by the larger cattle operators, this time as owners instead of lessors. Gradually the pitted and scarred landscape is resuming its proper function as a range region, but in the meantime, the loss, both in potential wealth and in human effort and happiness, has been appalling. Here again, as in the monotonous story of exploitation we have rehearsed, it is not possible to fix individual blame. Certainly not on the homesteaders, nor the cattlemen. Not on the well-meaning, humane politician whose name is associated with the experiment. Rather it rests upon a system which tolerates private privilege in utter disregard of public policy, and which as yet does not understand how science may be made to help in the determining of policy. At the time these measures were planned there were men who knew the Sand Hills from the scientific side, and who could have predicted exactly the outcome, but their views were not consulted in any effective way. Like the expert witnesses in our courts, scientists are only supposed to talk when they have arguments for, not against, a popular or influential project.

The Sand Hills, although not covered with short grass, but rather with bunch grasses, illustrate the situation in the true short-grass country, which extends from about the hundredth meridian west of the Rockies. In this country, of course, there are many fertile river bottoms where alfalfa and other crops can be grown. There are also many places which would prosper under irrigation, if the water could be made available. The Scottsbluff sugar beet area in western Nebraska is an example of this, as is much of the plain immediately along the front of the Rocky Mountains. But as for the bulk of the upland, its destiny is pasture, with the load of livestock nicely balanced to seasonal and local conditions. The cheapness with which extensive areas of this land could formerly be acquired was a temptation to speculators. "I saw the time," said an old banker, "when you could get a square mile of this for a pair of boots. The only trouble was, no one had the boots." Such were the conditions following a few years of the regularly re-curring drought. On the other hand, given a few years of good rainfall, which comes as inevitably as the years of drought, things brighten up, and upland crops may be tem-porarily successful. At such times speculators could unload, and did so, in smaller parcels than were safe for the purchaser to live on. Let the dry years return, as inevitably they will, and the plowed soil moves on with the whirlwind.

These conditions have been frightfully aggravated since the war by the introduction of power machinery and large-scale, upland farming, from western Texas north through the Dakotas. Let it be forever recorded that there was ample in-formation, based on the disastrous small-scale experiments which had been tried in western Kansas and Nebraska, to have forestalled the tragedy which occurred. But those were fabulous years, when the still, small voice of a President urg-ing economy and forethought was put down as a bit of New Englandism which should be laughed off and not allowed to interfere seriously with the general popularity of his quaint, canny character.

During these years, the nineteen-twenties, there were for a time good wheat prices and favorable rainfall in conjunction. Everything in the country was going full blast. It was the most natural thing in the world for the Panhandle farmers, whose cattle business had prospered during the war, and who had been encouraged to try dry farming, to attempt the growing of wheat on a huge scale. The soil was loose and friable, the land was theirs to use as they saw fit, gang plows and discs could be dragged across the level with astounding speed and ease by huge tractors. The wheat grew well—not more than knee-high, sometimes ankle-high, could be cut by a header and threshed all in one operation, leaving the short stubble standing until again disked under. Although the yield per acre was not high as compared with the eastern wheat land, the capital involved was less per acre, and the whole proceeding seemed very profitable. During thousands of years the slow growth of natural vegetation had stored considerable fertility in the soil. Amazing stories began to appear of the new era of power in agriculture—factory production applied to the land. As in the great spinning mills, where only one attendant was required to keep numbers of machines in smooth running order, here were huge farms which could be operated with ease by mechanical means. For a time it looked as though the small farmer of the eastern states would be driven out of business as surely as his brother who owned the small factory had been "merged" or exterminated. During these years there was actually an astonishing decrease in the number of acres of tilled land in the older states, and the murmur of discontent about the farm depression, which had been growing since the close of the war, swelled to a rumble which disturbed or delighted the politicians, according to their particular commitments. But out in the short-grass country, make no mistake about it, the wheat was being delivered.

Then, suddenly, everything collapsed. There was no market for the wheat. Even before this disaster, the wheat farmers, although making money, were grumbling. They felt that the manufacturing and shipping industries had been virtually handed gifts of money from the government. In the words of one of them: "Sure we are raising plenty of good wheat without a great deal of expense, and we are getting along. But these other fellows got rich, why can't we? If they can have money handed out to them by the working of a tariff and in other ways, why shouldn't we get all the traffic will bear?" This authentic comment shows that the "farm relief" business is one of many facets. Protest and distress are not always surely proportioned. Among the wheat farmers there was growing resentment against the marketing agencies, whose million-bushel elevators levied a charge of one cent per bushel per month for storage, but which after all were conducted with an eye to business and under conditions of severe competition. Cooperative storing and marketing agencies were organized, and after the destruction of the wheat market much wheat was stored out-of-doors in great heaps, where weevils, disease, and weather were free to work.

The causes of the disaster are involved with the whole question of the depression. Competition from other continents, and stagnation of the American foreign trade by high tariffs and European impoverishment were of course important factors. But the one undoubted fact of overproduction in this country is what concerns us here. To an important extent this was accomplished by the wholesale exploitation of the short-grass plains, whose permanent value for extensive grazing was a demonstrated fact, and whose permanent value as a dry farming center remained to be proved.

Artificial restoratives were applied to relieve the situation. These helped steady matters somewhat, but Mother Nature had a remedy of her own, as shortly appeared. Climate, which had been passing through the humid phase of its cycle, swung back towards the dry side. Months passed without a drop of rain in western Kansas in the summer of 1933. The next year was even worse. Not only did the wheat fail to mature, but so little grass was left unplowed that the livestock was starving, and had to be moved or killed. Buyers with a little cash could go through this country and name their own prices, sheep two bits apiece, cattle five to ten dollars. From the first of the drought there was considerable wind-sculpture of the naked fields, and local dust storms such as one finds in a dune area. But by the spring of 1935, these dust storms became matters of national extent, fitly symbolizing to distant Washington and New York the painful distress which existed in the country the dust came from. Whether the dust which fell in a given spot in the East actually came from the plowed-up pastures of the West, or from the desert itself, farther west, is immaterial. Within the newest wheat region fences hidden in dust, houses buried to the eaves, blinded jack rabbits, and suffering humanity were eloquent proof of the penalty incurred by disturbing nature's hard-won balance.

The drought, which was the apparent cause of the disaster, was certainly predictable—not in any exact sense, of course, but as unavoidably due to occur at intervals. A system of agriculture had been put into operation in disregard of the certain hazards of the short-grass region, and the dust storms became the costly, spectacular evidence of this fact.

The Great Pattern · VII

The Southwest of our continent is largely desert. The east coast is forest. As the forest stretches inland it gives way to grass. This girdle of grass separates forest from scrub and desert. Near the forest the grass is tall and lush, dotted with flowering herbs through the summer months and providing a surplus of nutritious pasture throughout the year. As it passes toward the desert the tall grass gives way to shorter kinds, scarcely shoetop high. Moving on through this one comes into the scrub, scattered clumps of woody brush which make the immediate fringe of the desert.

Such is the pattern one sees from the car window or airplane as he travels westward from the Atlantic coast in the United States. Naturally the pattern is often distorted and irregular. Where mountains rear their heights in the grassland country they are likely to be clothed with forest. Here and there in any province one may find types of exceptional soil on which are borne unexpected kinds of plant life.

The great belts of plant life are due principally to the moisture pattern. Temperature also has its effect at the extreme north and towards the equator. The effects of temperature, however, do not much concern us here. Practically speaking, the belts of forest, grassland, scrub, and desert, which we have described, are strips running from north to south across the United States. These strips beginning with the forest and ending with the desert have a climate which passes from humid through subhumid to semiarid and on into the arid desert.

Water, then, is largely the key to this pattern. This does

not necessarily mean the amount of rainfall, but rather the balance between rainfall and evaporation. For example, twenty inches of rain in Canada is sufficient to produce good forests, while in Mexico there are deserts which have at least twenty inches of rain per year. Although water is far from being the only requirement for plant life, it is an extremely important one, just as it is for animals. Even the driest of living plants contains an enormous percentage of water, and, in addition, a great deal of water passes from the root up through the living plant and out into the air. Man himself requires water in considerable amounts for his daily use. Under forced conditions an individual may survive if he can secure a few quarts each day, but in modern cities the amount of water used per capita each day ranges from fifty to two hundred seventy gallons. It is not commonly realized that the same water, properly purified each time, of course, must be used repeatedly by successive cities lining the banks of great rivers like the Ohio or Mississippi. The water pattern as such controls the pattern of human activity directly, as well as indirectly, through its influence on plants.

The vegetation which we have described did not spring into existence ready-made. The process is a matter of prolonged and constant change. Just as nature abhors a vacuum, it may be said that she will not tolerate idle surface on the earth. Whenever a new area is added to a continent in any fashion, the slow and endless process of covering it begins. Whether this new surface be rock, sand, or clay, there are venturesome kinds of plants, often very small and insignificant in appearance, which form the advance guard of nobler kinds. These pioneers may look like scales or tufts of living green, or, if the new surface is not solid rock, they may be our hardier and more familiar weeds. Whatever their type they slowly change the conditions of light, moisture, chemistry, and structure in the place where they grow. Like the true pioneer of the human race they do not thrive under the crowded conditions which their own activity has produced.

In consequence, they give way to other more tolerant kinds of plant life and the process continues.

At each stage there are appropriate types of animal life which fit into the growing community and are a necessary part of it. In addition there are many invisible forms of life whose activity is just as essential to orderly progress as that of the more conspicuous plants and animals. As time goes on the remains of dead organisms accumulate and by the action of the invisible bacteria are built into the growing soil, enriching it chemically and improving its physical texture. From this source comes the dark material known as *humus*, characteristic of rich and fertile soil.

The soil begins to assume a marked and definite character, depending partly on the kind of raw material at hand for its construction. But in even larger measure the character of the soil is stamped by the climate under which it forms. In the forests near the coast the abundant rainfall seeps down through the thin rich humus left by the forest leaves. It extracts from the soil below great quantities of lime and other easily dissolved materials. These later reappear in the springs and underground streams of hard water which are so common a feature in nature. These soluble materials are mostly alkaline. The material which is left is often acid and so too is frequently the humus which is on top. This is easy to understand if one remembers how ensilage and kraut sour through the formation of acids when they are allowed to stand. The soil at the other extreme of climate, namely the semiarid and arid regions, receives a relatively small amount of plant and animal material; this tends to dry rather than to ferment as in the forest regions. So little rain falls and so dry is the air that what water there is in the soil tends to be drawn to the surface, bringing with it the dissolved salts of lime, magnesium, and other alkaline material. In consequence, we often see in the drier parts of the country soils which are alkaline instead of acid. In many cases this alkali is not excessive in amount. It then serves to provide that abundance of needed minerals which enables the desert to blossom forth if water is supplied by irrigation, or whenever a brief infrequent rainy season may occur.

Between the desert and the forest, in subhumid grasslands, occur soil changes of the utmost importance to mankind. Here the abundant roots of the grass penetrate deeply into the soil and rot in place when they die. The dead leaves of the grass form a mulch or blanket which equalizes the movement of the water. There is neither a surplus of evaporation nor any violent percolation. Runoff and scouring are reduced to a minimum. The result is a layer of deep, rich, black soil of great fertility, neither excessively acid nor extremely alkaline. Besides the grasses there are many wild legumes such as lupines, vetches, and clovers, on whose roots are found bacteria which fix the nitrogen in the air into substances which greatly enrich the soil. The flesh and bones of the many grassland animals also add material such as phosphorus, which is of the utmost importance for plants.

From coast to desert, then, we see enacted this process of slow development. In each region it continues until a balance is reached. The kinds of plants and animals which are present at this stage are delicately adjusted to each other and to surrounding conditions. They perpetuate themselves because their young can thrive, unlike the young of weeds and other pioneers, under circumstances favorable to the adults. This condition is known as a *climax*, and where it obtains we see the resources of soil and plant life at their richest. One of the most important things about the climax stage is the fact that the soil now contains the largest possible amount of humus or broken-down plant and animal material.

The importance of this humus cannot be overemphasized. Besides containing its rich store of nutrient material it tempers the soil against extremes of wet and dry. It holds water like a sponge and keeps the water from scouring away the soil below and pouring turbid floods into the drainage streams. By it the water is slowly released, clear and limpid, to flow in even measure at all seasons of the year. In the drier regions the rôle of humus is equally important. Here the rains are less frequent but more apt to be torrential and hence destructive. Through the restraining action of humus the danger of flood with its disfiguring action on hill and valley is lessened. Furthermore, the evils of drought are tempered by the same sponge-like capacity to absorb water, thus keeping a reserve on hand to help tide over times of shortage. Clearly this makes a small amount of moisture go farther than it otherwise would. Man cannot control the amount of rain which falls but he can, by increasing the humus in his soil, secure the benefit which might come through increased rainfall. Conversely, if he destroys the humus he is in effect reducing the benefit which should come from the rain his land receives. In this sense it is no exaggeration to say that by increasing the humus a farm may be moved towards the seacoast; by decreasing it, the farm may be moved towards the interior.

In a state of nature where man has not interfered, the whole trend of development is such that the utmost benefit is received from whatever moisture happens to be available. By the addition of humus and the maturing of the soil the forest is enabled to move inland as far as possible. In fact, it crowds the grassland so closely that the margin is a scene of constant struggle. The slight advantage of a broken turf may allow trees to invade the prairie at this point. The inevitable prairie fire or occasional group of dry years will give grass the advantage at the expense of trees. Likewise, farther inland the grasslands encroach as far as possible upon the scrub and the scrub in turn upon the desert. At each zone of contact there is intense competition with the result that the natural desert is restricted to those severely dry regions in which the processes of nature are unable to conserve moisture sufficient for any luxuriant type of vegetation. Even the desert itself is not normally a lifeless place. Only where the combined severity of climate and soil are extreme do we find lifeless deserts.

The picture, then, of the continent undisturbed by man is one of the most abundant life possible. Forests extend far inland and the grass extends beyond them to its utmost possible limits. Deserts are shrunken to their least possible compass under the existing climatic conditions. In the midst of this order there is, of course, no absolute uniformity. Hilltops are drier and more exposed than valleys and ravines, although if it were not for the constant shiftings of the earth's crust the hills would be cut down and the valleys slowly built up. Within each province the drier and more exposed situations tend to have those kinds of vegetation which would occur in valleys farther inland. For example, the bur oak, which grows in stream valleys in Nebraska and Oklahoma, grows on very dry hilltops in Indiana. The shorter grasses which are found in eastern Colorado are also found on the drier hilltops in central Kansas. But here again the course of nature has its effect and as time goes on the pattern of vegetation in any place tends to become more and more uniform and appropriate to the climate. Even on the hilltops there is some accumulation of humus which makes possible to a considerable extent the upward climb of valley plants. Just as the desert in the interior comes to occupy the least possible space, so do the drier types of vegetation within each area.

The picture we have drawn is a fair description of the continent of North American when the white man entered upon it. There were, of course, extensive Indian cultures and in Mexico genuine civilization, but the primitive tools which the Indian possessed did not enable him seriously to disturb the general balance. Like the other living creatures, he fitted into the picture rather than dominated it. His agriculture, while sound and skillful, was necessarily casual and restricted. The more systematic and extensive agriculture of the mound builders had long since passed into oblivion. He depended largely upon game and fish but he made moderate use of these and all other resources about him. There is in the whole story of Indian economy nothing to compare with the ruthless, methodical, and finally successful extermination of the wild buffalo, the passenger pigeon, and the plains antelope. Even with the aid of the white man's railroad and high-powered firearms these great, enlightened, progressive, and humane measures required some time for their completion.

Observe the changes inaugurated with white settlement. The first point of contact was with the forest and its denizens. All the resources of European mechanical invention were brought to bear against nature. The forest was speedily stripped by every means at the command of civilized man. Its removal was not governed by the need for lumber. The sweep was clean; trees of all ages and sizes were destroyed. Nor were the immediate needs of the actual population for agricultural land considered. Every effort was made to produce a surplus for export without regard to maintaining any balance between need and supply, removal and return. We have already described the details of this relentless and extravagant march towards the interior of the continent. The forest which had been so slowly developed wherever trees could grow was destroyed. On land unfit for agriculture it was replaced either by grassland or by a second growth of pioneer and hence inferior type of forest. Moving west into the grasslands, with certain honorable exceptions, plow, fire, and overstocked herds of cattle did to the native grass what the ax and fire had done to the forests of the East. Here again there was considerable land not suitable to continuous agriculture. After the first wave of destruction, instead of returning to its original, bountiful crop of nutritious grass, it too was covered by inferior or pioneer types. The second-growth plants in the grassland area did not represent the best that the climate could produce in a state of nature. Instead they are akin to the drier, less desirable forms which composed the native vegetation still further inland. Actually the area of short grass, cactus, and scrub shifted eastward into what had been lush prairie.

Thus was broken the magic girdle which had thrown its green expanse about the shrinking desert. As time went on the further destruction wrought by man released the forces of wind and water which had been held in check. No longer was the surface protected against their action by a continuous carpet of plant life. Quickly the mantle of tempering soil with its sponge-like humus was washed and blown away from the uplands, lodging in the valleys, choking them with its new burden and concealing their rich alluvium. Gullies grew at the margins of the hills. Between what clumps of green were left appeared the color of the bare soil—the sure mark of the desert. In places the wash of wind and water scoured away everything that was loose, leaving floors of bare rock and pebbles not to be distinguished in their practical significance from the so-called desert pavements which mark the most barren and hopeless spots on the earth's surface.

Thus the white man in a few centuries, mostly in one, reversed the slow work of nature that had been going on for millennia. Thus have come the deserts, so long checked and held in restraint, to break their bonds. At every step the girdle of green about the inland deserts has been forced to give way and the desert itself literally allowed to expand. On the coast where once was forest the trees are gone. In the grassland which once was unbroken is inferior growth and much bare soil. Just as we have seen that under extremely favorable conditions the vegetation can move inland beyond its usual climatic limits, so now we see the process reversed. With the restraining influence of soil and vegetation broken, the desert moves outward from its proper climatic confine, and because of cultural or artificial conditions comes to occupy the place that rightfully belongs to other provinces.

The laws which govern the development of soil and vegetation are as inescapable as the laws of the conservation of energy and of matter upon which they are based. No matter how complex or seemingly mysterious the operations of the organic world, they are still based upon cause and effect. It is as impossible to get something for nothing as it is to make water run uphill. If man destroys the balance and equilibrium demanded by nature, he must take the consequences. There is no magic which will undo the mischief he has wrought.

Cold Figures · VIII

A noble parable in one of the old storybooks has to do with four children on a hilltop, discussing the ownership of a big red apple. Only after the apple had slipped out of greedy fingers and rolled downhill into the mouth of a hungry cow did three of the children realize that the fourth was right in suggesting that the apple could be cut into four parts and passed around.

> *"I wish, said the First and the Second and Third,*
> *We had kept it and cut it in four."*

With this simple but somber lesson in mind, let us see just how much apple we have, and how many mouths have claim upon it. And as we do it might be well to have an inventory of the condition of the apple—wormy places and rotten spots, and bruised patches where grasping fingernails have dug too deeply.

In the way of statistics we now have an imposing amount of information, whose collection, begun during the preceding administration, has been completed and presented in the recent report of the National Resources Board. In this report is an analysis of population, land, forests, water, and minerals from the standpoint of past changes, present conditions, and future developments. What story do the figures tell?

The area of the United States is 1,903 million acres, of which about 413 million are in crops, good, bad, and indifferent. Of this huge empire just a little over half is in farms, a little over one-fifth is in forest, less than a fifth is in grassland at the present time. One twenty-fifth is of no use, practically speaking, although some of it can be made useful. About one-thirtieth is devoted to special uses other than agriculture or forestry; for example, nearly one per cent of the land area of the United States is occupied by public roads of one sort or another. The remainder of the special portion is composed of cities, homesites, right of ways, and the like.

So much for the size of the apple. We shall have something to say of its condition later. How many claimants are there? The first census, taken in 1790, showed about four million people in the United States, which was, of course, much smaller in area than it is today. The census of 1930 recorded about 123 million; that of 1940 about 132 million. Where and how will this end?

About 1820 the birth rate began a slow and steady drop, which has continued ever since, although the total number of births per year increased for almost exactly one hundred years thereafter—until 1921—because the population kept growing through immigration. Following 1921, in a period of three years there were 750,000 fewer births. It is interesting to compare birth rates over the United States today with those of the past. An isolated mountain county in Kentucky still has the same birth rate which the whole country had in 1820, while certain selected cities of almost pure American stock have less than the present average national birth rate. Thus marked is the effect of improved living conditions on the rate of human increase. A few years ago a sensible British biologist pointed out to agitators who wished to persecute a certain racial group, depriving them of privileges, that the surest way to lessen the danger was to give the undesired (not necessarily undesirable) group every opportunity to succeed and prosper. Under such conditions the birth rate inevitably must fall and the group diminish in numerical importance as time goes on.

It is generally assumed that the city standard of living is better than the rural. This might be honestly questioned, particularly by those who prefer rich cream to blue milk, fresh fruits and vegetables to those which are wilted or canned, and pure air which comes as a matter of course instead of as the reward of a holiday or a luxury obtained at the price of membership in a golf club. Be that as it may, the cities of this country fall short of maintaining their own population through births by about one-third. The rural districts, on the other hand, produce one-half more than enough to maintain themselves at their present population. This interesting fact shows how the cities of today, as of all times past, are necessarily recruited from the country population. It also illustrates one of the difficulties which have to be dealt with in the task of predicting our future population. After all, we must know how many mouths there will be to feed in another century. Even if one agrees with the remark attributed to Uncle Joe Cannon, "Posterity never did anything for me, and I don't propose to do anything for it," it might be amusing to know what chance one's grandchildren have of starving to death. And the visible concern in political circles over the future suggests that to many people the matter is not one to be dismissed lightly. Whatever else may be wrong with the politician, he is a good mind reader.

While the precise course of future population cannot be charted, there is some agreement as to the ultimate outcome— a stationary population, with births and deaths approximately balancing. Just how soon this condition will be reached depends upon a number of things: for instance, how industrial conditions will permit the city and country population to be distributed. If manufacturing picks up, more people will go into the cities, where the birth rate, as we have seen, is lower. If there are not many jobs, people will have to stay in the country, or move back to it, grow their own food, and have more children than they would in town. The number of immigrants will make a difference, too, for the newcomers themselves not only increase the count, but have large families. On this score, the signs point toward an increasing restriction upon immigration, to the point where there will soon be little net gain from this source. Stationary populations have already developed in France and the Scandinavian countries, while the abrupt trend in this direction among the British during the past twelve years has been amazing.

As to the United States, estimates of maximum population are now uncertain, but they exceed the 200 million we used to hear about. Between 1920 and 1936 the birth rate dropped from 23.7 to 16.7 and deaths from 13.0 to 11.6. With World War II the birth rate has risen. The death rate has not. But it is a fair guess that births will steadily decrease during the next two decades. Although the final outcome, a stationary population, seems fairly certain, the speed with which it will materialize will be powerfully influenced by the trend of government policy with regard to contraception. If the establishment of clinics and the spread of information is legalized, the birth rate will drop promptly, otherwise more slowly, but just as surely through the spread of underground information and practice. At present influences are pressing the government on both sides of this question, both animated by powerful moral purpose. Thus far industry and strong economic groups have not taken sides. If they do, the pressure may decide the issue, as with prewar political issues in Germany and Italy.

Even with the 150 million mistakenly assumed a short two decades ago for 1960, the United States would have had a population of almost fifty souls to the square mile. In other words, there would have been about fourteen acres of land per person in this country. Of course this does not all represent cropland. On the 150 million population basis, and at the time the estimate was made, there were about 460 million acres, or slightly more than three acres per person, forecast for 1960, a figure which tallied closely with what experts then regarded as necessary to maintain the American standard of living. Today, with the population up by perhaps thirty millions, the arable land per person is appreciably reduced. The exact acreage required depends of course upon many factors, such as fertility, intensiveness, and number of domestic animals which are necessary to farming operations. It takes more land to feed a horse than to feed a man, but the horse's board must be charged upon the man's board bill. Other factors will be the diet requirements, already changing because of a better understanding of nutrition and the diminished amount of physical labor performed by the average person. Still further changes are in store as the proportion of old people to young increases, which it must continue to do. The need for land to raise agricultural exports is another factor, although it now seems unlikely that we shall ever again become a great exporter of staple foods. We shall probably continue to be an important factor in the world market of cotton, tobacco, and fruit. However, since our agricultural imports of rubber, bananas, and coffee come from the tropics, they do not relieve our own land of pressure.

The demands of our population being then roughly certain, in what condition are we to meet them? In what condition are the 460 million acres of cropland? What reserve of unused land is there to be tapped if some that is at present farmed has to be abandoned? What possibility is there of apportioning the land to most economical use, and of maintaining its fertility?

The experts who have been called to Washington and given a free rein to dream out an ultimate land policy see little possibility of increasing the percentage of land that is to be productive in terms of agriculture, grazing, or forestry. In fact they look forward to a slight decrease in this sort of acreage, despite a decrease from about 4 to approximately 3 per cent in the land which is now of little or no use. The land now useful but not productive, such as that in public works, cities, etc., is expected to increase from about 3 to about 6 per cent of our total area. Roughly, then, the proportions will be about as they now are.

If the total land area of the United States is graded according to quality, the results are somewhat as follows:

Grade 1	Excellent	5.3 per cent
Grade 2	Good	11.1 per cent
Grade 3	Fair	18.1 per cent
Grade 4	Poor	19.1 per cent
Grade 5	Unfit	46.4 per cent

With the exception of certain undrained swamplands, some lands probably suited to irrigation, and some cut-over forest lands of dubious permanent value for agriculture, it is probably safe to say that farming has been tried out everywhere. In fact, these costly experiments have been pushed far beyond the margin of conceivable safety. Land has reverted to pasture only where the impossibility of cropping has been overwhelming, and the pasture given back to forest only when there was plainly no chance of making it pay as pasture.

Thirty-five million acres of former cropland are now obviously unfit for that purpose. In the ten years following the end of World War I 33 million acres were released from tillage. During the same period there were placed under cultivation in the dry plains about 30 million acres of new land, much of which has by now clearly shown itself unfit for the purpose and will be released, or has been since the last census. In fact more than a little of it has been moved out of the picture to parts unknown, on the wings of the wind.

Half of the farms in this country, in 1929, sold less than a thousand dollars worth of products each, and many of them a good deal less. It is not generally appreciated, perhaps, that a considerable portion of our farmers produce and sell little if any more than the typical European peasant. Four hundred and fifty thousand farms, a total of seventy-five million acres, are recommended for retirement from agriculture, as being incapable of supporting those who work them. A Chinese might see in this something of the same baffling western philosophy that prompts an American to buy a pig, squealing bloody murder because it is being dragged along by a rope around its leg, and then out of kindness kill the pig to release it from its suffering. But of course the present case is slightly different. The same benevolent government which permitted or even encouraged settlement on the land in the first place and practically gave it away, will now proceed to buy it back and translate the suffering owner to fairer fields—not kill him. A decided difference in fact.

One-third of the unprofitable farms is cropland, an amount of 25 million acres. Now 25 million acres to be taken away from the present 460 million of arable land is no small portion, particularly when we recall that all of the 460 million are to be needed not later than 1960. In fact, it will not be enough merely to replace 25 million acres of cropland, the amount needed being, for various reasons, more nearly 55 million. Where will it come from?

We have already seen that practically everything possible in the way of arable land has been tried. But, like the comedian at the keyhole, we are permitted to exclaim, "What will they think of next?" Of course there is swampland, like the Everglades, which can be drained and put under cultivation, even though the Everglades have a fairly definite value to human society as they are. There is also more land that can be irrigated. Yet, it must be admitted that irrigation projects have not always turned out to be economically successful heretofore, apart from the disastrous rates of silting of some of the large reservoirs due to erosion within the watershed. There is also the possibility of supplemental irrigation in the moister regions—capable, it is estimated, of increasing the effective farm area by as much as 17 per cent.

Tapping these various resources to the limit, it is believed that the deficit will have to be made up by the plowing of land now in pasture. This is not a matter of plowing virgin soil, but in large measure reclaiming for tillage land which has been allowed to lapse into pasture because it could not pay its way with crops. This will involve the double burden of building it up, and of increasing the carrying capacity of such pastures as are left, by expensive fertilization. We may not be as badly off as the arctic explorer who is reduced to chewing on his moccasins to stay alive, but we have certainly used up all the surplus stores we had, and are facing a situation where we shall have to work to keep the larder full.

Since the balance is to be restored at the expense of farm pastures, it might be well to look into the question of the great natural pastures in the western grassland. We have already shown how these have suffered at the hand that rocks the plow. The great western livestock industry which developed so rapidly after the Civil War had by 1885 seriously overloaded the range. Except on privately held land there was no proper check, and as a result the range steadily deteriorated, notably so after 1900. In addition to depletion of the food supply, a major erosion problem developed. On the Navajo reservation, for example, conditions have recently become so serious as to threaten the whole industrial setup, as well as huge irrigation projects which drain from the area.

There are, it is estimated, in the United States well over one billion acres of pasture of all sorts, but mostly western. Of the western, over three-fourths is not subjected to controlled grazing and is now being depleted by overstocking, fire, and unwise attempts at cultivation. Recently, for a period of about fifteen years, former dryland farms were reverting to pasture at the rate of nearly a million acres per year. But the process of reëstablishment of the native sod is slow and uncertain at best. Even in the more humid grasslands from five to thirty years may be required. In eastern Wyoming the wagon ruts from the Overland Trail, long since abandoned, are still marked by a different shade of green from the grass about them. During the long intervals before the sod is restored, there is ample time for erosion, both by water and by wind, just as there is in the wake of fire or overgrazing. In the face of generally deteriorated pastures, both on eastern farms and western ranges, then, there is the absolute need for more cultivated land at the expense of pasture, and for a 10 per cent increase in pasture capacity by 1960.

Only God can make a Tree

The poet has short cuts to truth which are denied the plodding man of science. The heading of this chapter has been vulgarized into sticky, repulsive sentiment, smearing out of sight the beautiful wisdom which it expresses. The poet has told the truth, in his own idiom, to be sure, but truth nevertheless. It makes little difference whether one looks upon the tree with the appraising eye of the lumberman, in terms of board feet, or with the eye of the artist, as a glorious blend of symmetry, light, shade, and color, or with the slightly jaundiced eye of the scientist, as a marvelous, intricate laboratory whose workings are a perpetual, unsolved challenge. The growth of tree from seed takes time and nurture amid conditions which it has been the perverse and needless genius of man to destroy.

The symphonic story of destruction has been caught up by one voice after another, until it should be known to every ear that hears. From its first statement as a timely warning note, a century ago, through decades of futile, baffled protest by naturalists, tree-lovers and public-spirited citizens, it did not gather effective volume until the reign of Theodore Roosevelt. Roared forth by him and Pinchot in stentorian duet, it shook an apathetic nation into action. Forest conservation became a definite feature of our public policy. Immediately, huge reservations of the public domain were created, and the Forest Service was built into an effective arm of government.

So effective and notable has been the work of the Forest Service, and so manifest the interest of the government in the problem of forestry, that many citizens have more or less dismissed the problem from their minds. The same thing has happened with forestry that happened to public interest in food and drug regulation after Wiley's efforts had secured the passage of regulative measures. Or the case might be compared to public indignation with regard to trusts after the passage of the Sherman legislation. Once the public knows that machinery has been established to correct an evil, it settles back to a condition of complacency, assuming that Uncle Sam will do the job. Partly this is due to inertia, of course, but more largely to a misunderstanding of how government must work in a democracy.

While the people regard their task as completed with the passage of good legislation, predatory interests which are hampered by the legislation look upon their own task as being nicely started. They are immediately put in the position of knowing all the rules under which their enemy, society, must carry on the combat. Although actually representing minorities, they are powerful, and they never settle back to sleep. The stakes in the game are high, and justify unceasing attention. Ceaselessly, therefore, they look for loopholes, applying pressure here, craft and stealth there, until the program which had seemed adequate to protect the well-being of the people for all time is as full of holes as a sieve. Furthermore, conditions are constantly changing because of perfectly legitimate and inevitable factors, changing enough to require on that score alone constant vigilance from those who would keep the works in repair.

In point of morale and high devotion, skillful management of obstacles, and technical efficiency, the Forest Service of the United States is probably not surpassed by any other arm of government. The worst that can be said of it is that perhaps, on a few occasions, it has put forth propaganda which was somewhat questionable from the standpoint of science. The famous dispute with the Weather Bureau as to whether forests actually increase the rainfall is the principal, perhaps the only, illustration of this. It has possibly been a little too sanguine at times about the lack of injury in some of the areas under its control on which regulated grazing has been practiced. It has embarked on extensive planting experiments which did not succeed, but in one such case at least did so only in response to pressure from competent scientific sources. On the other hand it has candidly, even hazardously, published the results of investigation which upset its earlier policies, and which might, if misunderstood, seriously cripple its own work. For example, it has found that fire, so generally the enemy of the forest, may have actual value in parts of the United States as an instrument of silviculture, particularly in relation to pine forests.

That the aims and ideals of our forest policy are still unrealized is in no sense a failure of the Forest Service. Instead it is a failure of the general public to appreciate the obstacles under which that Service works. And in so far as the public is ignorant, it is so largely because of the conditions under which the Forest Service has been obliged to work in order to get results. One of the more admirable and effective things about the Service is the patience and diplomacy with which it has dealt with interests vested by law and custom. These interests might be in the form of huge commercial lumbering concerns which had to be won over slowly to the view of forest utilization rather than exploitation; or they might be in the form of small squatters who live by foraging on their environment; or they might be, and often were, cattle and sheep men whose stock had ranged the national domain at scarcely any cost to themselves, and without restriction. The public itself, in search of recreation, has afforded a problem of great magnitude. Here, while firmness and even retribution have been visited upon the careless and thoughtless, a conciliatory and hospitable attitude has prevailed. To the average traveler who visits the forests today, no sight is more welcome than the green of the ranger's uniform, and no hand more helpful than his. The forester has even had at times to drag the dead weight of overly sentimental tree-lovers, who cannot envision the forest as primarily a thing to be of use to man. For just as there are booklovers who think books are to look at, and not into, so there are people who confuse a forest with a museum. It so happens that any tree will, in the course of time, reach a point of maximum value, after which it declines and dies. Sound forest management demands that trees be harvested when ripe, with as little injury as possible to those which remain, and it also recognizes that there are weeds among trees, just as among smaller plants. Such weeds, in the interest of better sorts, must be kept out.

These then, represent some of the many interests whose impact upon the Forest Service has slowed down its beneficent efforts. To be perfectly clear as to what is meant when we say that our forest policy has failed to achieve its ends, let us recall that we still cut twice as much timber as we grow, each year, and that we use even more—five times as much as we grow, to be exact. No nation which does that, with five hundred million acres of forest land at its disposal, has any right to cry success. Nor do even the most sanguine prophets of a new order believe that we will be able, before several more decades, to place ourselves upon a sustaining basis, even if all of the present suggestions for more adequate management go into effect.

Just what is wrong? In the first place, the areas of forest under government control consist very largely of land that no one else cared enough about to grab, during the heyday of passing out something for nothing. Included is much land that cannot by any stretch of the imagination produce commercially profitable timber. Also there are areas of good merchantable timber, but so remote from markets and transportation that they are not of commercial significance. Yet the proper care of these great tracts is almost as much of a burden as though they were economically self-supporting. Often, in the interests of the watersheds which they protect, it is imperative that they be attended to. There are, in addition, areas which were once in private hands, but which have reverted after having been exploited in such a way that, not only is the crop of timber destroyed, but the possibility of profitable reforestation has become extremely remote. The cream has been stripped, and generally speaking, the Forest Service has blue milk on its hands.

With regard to the great private holdings in whose management the government is coöperating, few people realize what is involved. Government bears about two-thirds of the cost of protection on these units, but the corporations holding them retain practically all of the old despotic privileges of irresponsible private ownership. They are counseled, of course, to cut only ripe timber, to leave ample seed trees, and otherwise practice the sort of management which would secure a perpetual, steady yield of profitable timber. But there is nothing to prevent the owners, at any time their temporary advantage seems to justify, from stripping the ground clean and leaving it to the mercy of the elements. Certainly there is no means at present to compel them to cut with any regard for the future.

Under such a handicap, the Forest Service carries on in coöperation with private owners, who control, by the way, some 70 per cent of the forest area of the country today. An encouraging sign has been the slow increase in the number of private owners who have been willing to coöperate with the government and adopt improved management. But this has come about through grim necessity rather than from any sense of social responsibility. Decidedly, they are not in business for their health.

There have been times, of course, when individuals in the Forest Service have slipped the leash and struck out fiercely at the abuses of private ownership. But in the main there has been a patient, tactful policy of steady conciliation which has done good work. The only trouble is that from the standpoint of society, the patient may be dead by the time the cure is in a position to be effective. This is the viewpoint of one of the most concise and effective of many presentations of the forest problem which has yet appeared—*The People's Forests*, by Robert Marshall. This book not only attacks the abuses of private ownership, but the institution itself, so far as applied to forests, and suggests a policy of gradual alienation of them into government hands.

Besides the obstacle of private ownership, there is the grazing problem. The average citizen probably pictures a forest as consisting solely of trees and wild animals. In point of fact the tame animals, both in privately and publicly owned forests, are a major factor. So great was the expansion of the livestock industry during the second half of the last century, that the use of forests as range ground was written into the custom of the stockman as a matter of course. There are no fences about the forests strong enough to keep out herds of cattle, and none can be made. Forestry then has had to develop a tolerance for the situation, and has been fortunate when grazing fees and a measure of regulation could be established. When fees are obtained they are more nominal than real, even though they may add up to a large amount for the country as a whole. The forests are pastures, first, last, and foremost. To make them otherwise would bring on a battle worse than that which accompanied the enclosure of the commons in Europe—a situation many people do not appreciate.

Trees, like grass, have ever been a source of food for animals, and both are adjusted to a moderate tax from that source. But young trees differ from grass, in that a single mouthful taken from them may cause permanent injury. The tender growing point of the grass is protected well down inside the plant. In the tree it is fully exposed. To some extent the herds of animals in the forest browse on the lower branches of taller trees, but in their sweep across the ground they take grass, herbs, and tender seedlings of trees without much discrimination. The effect of this on forest reproduction is obvious.

So ruinous it is that the average farm wood lot is often worth-less as a forestry enterprise—no young trees ever get a start to replace the older ones.

Here, again, the Forest Service has cheerfully accepted the handicap and done its best with a bad situation. It has become the greatest livestock concern in the United States. There are not a few foresters who have more to do directly with sheep and cattle than they do with trees. The Forest Service has done some distinguished work on the problem of range man-agement. It has studied the effects of different types of grazing on the innumerable types of forest with which it has had to deal. The carrying capacity at different seasons, that is, the number of head of livestock to an acre, the effect upon young trees and upon the grass about them, have all been studied with great care. Then slowly this information has been used to work out a policy in relation to the cattle industry. Here the greatest caution has been necessary. A single false move, and the patient work of years might be undone. Throughout, the attitude has been taken that grazing is an inevitable obligation upon the forest, and persuasion, rather than compulsion, has been used to establish it upon the least harmful basis.

It would be idle to pretend that even today, under the most advanced and successful management, the forests do not suf-fer from this dual use. There are many places, notably in the Rocky Mountains, where the forest is not coming back as it should. With the bland and imperturbable tact which is a part of their code, the foresters will point out the infrequence of good seed years and of good years for seed germination as contributing causes. But anyone who does not labor, as they do, under the necessity of placating the livestock interests can recognize that grazing, even though strictly regulated, is playing its part in this delay.

Along with other difficult problems of forest and range management, the Forest Service is obliged to devote a great proportion of its resources to the problem of fire. In the dense, inflammable conifer forests of the North and West occur the devastating crown fires, which tear along furiously consuming everything in their path. So dreaded are they that even the most ignorant are not likely to set them going wilfully. The chief difficulty comes from carelessness of tourists, lightning, and accident. However, in the relatively open pine and oak forests of the Southeast, there is a different story. Here the general type of fire is the surface fire, which ambles along among the grass and dead leaves, licking its way around the bases of the tree trunks, sometimes ascending them, sometimes not. The whole thing seems harmless enough, particularly since the larger standing trees are not often killed outright. Such fires leave the forest clear of underbrush, and the ground so burned is covered with green, succulent-looking grass early the following spring. Little wonder then that firing the woods has come to be an annual ritual with the small farmers who eke out a precarious living in the cleared valleys and depend upon the woods around them to furnish pasture for their cattle as well as mash for their lean-figured swine. So ingrained is the practice of deliberate burning that it has come to be regarded as a panacea—even being credited with helping to control typhoid, malaria, and the cattle tick.

Of course the custom is on no higher a level of merit than the rest of the farm operations practiced by these isolated, struggling, and handicapped people. The large standing timber is really injured by fire scars at the base of the trunks, which provide an entrance for internal decay. The younger seedlings are generally killed outright, and the forest prevented from reproducing. Nests of game birds are destroyed. The improvement of the pasture itself is likely to be more apparent than real, through the gradual substitution of weeds for the original nutritious vegetation, although there is some evidence that under properly managed burning this may not be true. Moreover, there is an inevitable damage through the destruction of the rich black leaf-mold on the surface, and consequent impoverishment of the soil. The soil is able to hold less water than before, so that runoff and scouring are promoted. At Guthrie, Oklahoma, are two patches in the oak forest of equal size, one unburned, the other very skillfully and lightly burned once a year, when the ground is moist. To the unpracticed eye there is little difference. Both are covered with green grass. But when the rain falls on both, twenty-eight times as much of it runs off the burned patch as the unburned, and ten times as much soil is carried away by it.

With its characteristic skill and farsighted practice, the Forest Service has approached the control of the habitually incendiary fires of the Southeast. In addition to systems of fire towers (which the natives would have dynamited had they not learned that their purpose was the detection of forest fires, not of illicit stills) and the usual organization, selected men were sent into the area with portable motion picture outfits. The repertoire of films contained a judicious combination of comedies and other entertainment along with films showing graphically just what the results of fire are. So effective has this been, particularly among the younger generation, that material reduction in fires has resulted. But there is still a great deal of trouble. Unemployed who see a chance to pick up a little cash fighting fires are not above furnishing an occasion for their own employment. Hard-shelled oldsters, not to be shaken from the custom of generations, refuse to be converted. It is useless to arrest them, for they must be tried before juries of their neighbors. Finally, it happens that a huge portion of these lands which the government is trying to protect do not belong to it, but to big lumber operators. More often than not, there is no love lost between the mill owners and the scattered farm population. Not a few fires have their origin in this hostility. Government propaganda regarding the injury done by fires in this case merely suggests a means of striking effectively at the industrialists. It is safe to say that until the lumbering industry in these states realizes its social responsibility to the rural citizen and makes it mutually unprofitable to burn the woods, incendiary fires will continue. Because of its favorable climate, the southeastern area represents one of the most hopeful centers of permanent timber supply in the United States, and it is to the interest of the country at large to demand that the production of timber and conservation of soil there be put on an economical basis.

One generation has seen lumber advance from fifteen dollars to eighty-five or more a thousand. Millions are living in worse houses than they should be, with poorer finish and less desirable furniture than is proper, all because of the timber famine produced by our own extravagant waste. The problem of forest conservation touches every pocketbook in the nation, and affects the standard of living of everyone. No one needs to be persuaded of this; but there is acute need for everyone to realize just what is involved in trying to achieve an effective, working program.

Leaves of Grass · X

Man, if there were no grasses, would be just one of the animals. No plants but the grasses can endure the continued nibbling of grazing beasts; to a degree they actually thrive on it. Without roving herds of quadrupeds, primitive man would have had no means of livelihood except those afforded by the fish and game of the forest, and the fruits and roots which grow there. By domestication, the grazing animals enabled him to move forward into a pastoral existence. Moreover, in the domestication of certain highly favorable grasses, man found bread, repose from unceasing movement, and ultimately civilization. As we have seen elsewhere, there is a definite connection between the first centers of civilization and the origin of the culture of rice, wheat, and maize, all of them grasses.

No one would deny to the grasses the credit they deserve for their rôle in elevating mankind from the beasts, although we have seen how dismal is the treatment accorded our grazing lands and the soil upon which our bread must grow. Yet there is another reason why the grasses deserve well of man. The great grasslands, apart from the abundant wealth they yield, are the strategic buffer between civilization and the desert. While there are notable exceptions, the great centers of population are in regions whose climate would, if given a chance, produce forest. From there humanity shades out to virtual invisibility in the desert. We may pass from Massachusetts, with over five hundred people to a square mile, west to Oklahoma, with thirty-four, on through Arizona, with about three, into Nevada, which has less than one. If numbers mean anything, they tell a story here. It is not good to have the deserts grow in size. And against that growth our best defense is the tight-knit turf of the grasslands. Such being the situation, it may be well to know more about them.

Grass, unlike forest, has not long had friends who were organized into potent groups. While the country can number its trained foresters by the thousands, the men who understand the technical problems of the grasslands are a few score at most, and these are largely interested in the grazing aspects. Of course, the reason is not hard to understand. When a tree is cut it leaves "a hole in the sky." When forests are destroyed every one is aware of that fact. Even when the forest deteriorates one does not need to be a trained forester to sense what is taking place. And when the price of lumber goes out of bounds the situation speaks for itself, the commercial products of the forest being essential to all of us.

Grass, on the other hand, is to most people simply a green carpet. The kinds of plants, their abundance, and their vitality are matters which escape the casual. So long as all is green, all is well. To the untrained traveler the great grasslands are a matter of indifference or even an unutterable bore as he moves through them, in automobile or train. The term "Great American Desert" was not coined for the desert at all, but for that land which was, to the writer of *My Antonia*, alive and glowing with beauty.

"As I looked about me I felt that the grass was the country, as the water is the sea. The red of the grass made all the great prairie the color of winestains, or of certain seaweeds when they are first washed up. And there was so much motion in it; the whole country seemed, somehow, to be running."

The grass affects our pocketbooks only through the operation of a chain of physiology, technology, and economics, upon which many other factors impinge. The result is that when the price of meat soars too high because of a failure of pasture we express our resentment, not by organizing to conserve the grasslands, but by voting out the old congressman, governor, or president, and voting in the new. As immediate logic this is of course execrable, but it may not be so bad in the long run if the politicians are shrewd enough to see what really lies back of the trouble. The terrific dust storms which today choke the nostrils and dim the sky may be worth their cost if they focus our attention upon the grasslands, so that we may indelibly understand that they are as vital to our own highly developed civilization as they ever were to Abraham, the lord of flocks and herds, dwelling in his tent.

The Europeans who first explored America came of a stock in whose tradition all influence of a steppe or grassland environment had long since disappeared. Their first glimpses of great expanses of natural grass or "prairie" as they called it, amazed them. And on through to very recent times, the explanation of this kingdom without trees has intrigued the scientific and popular imagination. There is really an imposing list of theories as to the "cause" of the prairies—fire, soil, grazing, as well as climate having been suggested. All of these, and other influences as well, may play a part under appropriate conditions but we know today that the principal factor is climate. As a rough and ready expression of this, forests tend to occur where there is a greater annual fall of rain in inches than the air, on the average, will draw back in evaporation. Where the reverse is true grassland occurs, or if the evaporation is still more intense, scrub and desert. Refined studies of the relation between rainfall, evaporation, and temperature, as well as their seasonal pattern, give us a map of North American climate showing remarkable similarity to the vegetation map.

We have said that the average person looks on grass as merely a green carpet, studded, on occasion, with flowers. But just as the loving eye of a connoisseur, roaming frequently over his treasured Persian weaves, will detect new beauties of design within design, so with the man who knows the grassland. For him it is a pattern of infinite richness. So overwhelming is its variety that long years of patient study have been required to see order and law behind the apparent chaos. Yet certainly order and law are there.

From the infinitude of possible sounds which strike the ear, some eighty-odd intervals of pitch compose the keyboard of the piano. Give a musician these and he will evolve a wilderness of beauty. There are thousands of kinds of plants which may be found in the grass country. But its real character is determined by the way a few score of dominant species are deployed by nature to fit the vagaries of earth and atmosphere. The grasses themselves fall conveniently into three groups, according to height—tall, medium, and short, with roots whose depth is in proportion to their tops. These are distributed according to the abundance of available moisture, whether it be conditioned by climate, soil, or topography. Just as the maize of the Iowa farmer is taller than he, while that of the Hopi Indian is scarcely knee high, so it is with the native grasses. The tall kinds flourish in the humid eastern prairies, the short in the dry western plains, with the medium between. Or if, in any part of the grasslands, conditions of soil and topography produce sufficient degrees of difference in the moisture supply, the various types of grass may be found growing not far apart, each in its appropriate place. Even under uniform conditions there is usually a mixture. Then in wetter years, the taller grasses dominate the scene, in drier periods the shorter kinds flourish best. So flexible is this battery of plant life, and so profound its resources for meeting all of the possible vicissitudes of its habitat, that it is seldom caught off guard. Unlike the fields planted by man, where the outcome is staked on a single kind of crop, there is little or no chance for complete failure. In a particular year, cultivated crops may bring much richer returns than native grass, of course, and often do so. But year in and year out, the yield of the grassland is sure—that of the planted fields, never. The crops are like speculative securities, the wild grassland like government bonds of a nation whose pledge is sacred. No accountant is needed to analyze the type of enterprise into which American grassland agriculture has let itself. Instead of there being an ample reserve of native grass on each farm, it is difficult, increasingly so, to find areas which are suitable for study. Two specialists engaged on a study of tall-grass prairie in the upper Mississippi basin were obliged to travel thirty thousand miles and resort to hide-and-seek methods in order to locate satisfactory specimens of this vanishing vegetation. The unbroken, virgin prairie sod is on its way to join the dodo. In the face of what is common knowledge, statistics on this subject can be waved aside with the formula of objecting counsel as redundant, irrelevant, and immaterial.

The drier types of grassland, occupied by medium and short grass, have suffered less than the humid, tall-grass province from the direct inroads of the plow, although their increasing destruction from this source has been an undoubted major factor in the recent, serious, dust storms. What has been said of the speculative character of ordinary farming applies even more strongly to them than to the moister areas.

The plow, most thoroughgoing and irrevocable in its work of the agents of change, is not the only one. With it must be considered two other influences which have ever been operative in the grasslands, but whose effect, until the advent of the white man, was on the whole moderate and beneficent. Fire and grazing are a part of the normal experience to which natural grasslands are adjusted, along with the fluctuations of climate and the variations of soil and landscape. Unless utilized fully by normal grazing, the medium and tall grasses produce a surplus of dry growth which rapidly accumulates, insulating the soil from the warming rays of the sun and obstructing the growth of new seasons. Because the air is drier than in forest regions, this surplus of dead material above ground does not readily rot down to form humus in the soil. Under such conditions it appears that fire at infrequent intervals may actually be of service, with benefits outweighing any damage it might cause. Certainly there is plenty of evidence of such fires, not only those set by Indians before the white man came, but even those of geologic time, when atmospheric causes such as lightning or meteorites furnish the torch. The very fact that both grazing and fire can be beneficial has made the problem of their rational control under crowded modern conditions a very difficult one. And their evil effects are the more sinister because, as explained in an earlier chapter, they are not immediately apparent. Persistent overgrazing and repeated burning inaugurate, not prompt desolation, but instead a slow insidious change in composition, ultimately reducing the total yield as well as the food value. Stock-poisoning trouble more often than not starts with overgrazing. There is more room for poisonous plants to become established and more temptation for the stock to eat them in the absence of highly palatable forage. Thorns and spines enable the plants which have them to persist in spite of overgrazing, and ultimately to spread, thus increasing the number of that sort of inedibles.

The plants of the virgin sod are mostly perennials—coming up year after year from the same underground system. Once established, they depend much less upon seeds than upon new buds for their spread. This in fact is one of the most important features of that marvelous flexibility of the grasslands which we have mentioned. Each individual clump is prepared to put forth few or many new shoots each year, as conditions happen to permit, or even to suspend operations for a time and live upon its underground store. Under too frequent attacks from fire or hungry teeth the clumps of grass cannot hold their own. Shrinking in size, they leave space for brash, short-lived annual weeds of little food value. These may be in turn followed by more persistent and even more useless perennial weeds, such as the poisonous or thorny types mentioned above. All too often, if the abuse is continued, nothing can come into the tortuous spaces between the clumps in time to prevent the elements from scouring them into winding channels. It is not uncommon to find a once beautiful and uniform sod which has been reduced to isolated tufts or bunches, each standing several inches above the eroded bare surfaces that separate them. There is a kind of grass which finally comes into these naked spaces after the topsoil is gone and erosion has done its worst which the natives call "poverty grass." Its dirty, pale gray will show in patches across the landscape for miles, a warning to any intelligent investor except those hardy souls who deal in royalties for wealth far below the soil.

Can the grassland, once disturbed, be restored? If destroyed, can it return? Apparently so, but the greater the destruction, as a rule, the longer the time and the greater the effort required. The underground parts of a great many of the native plants have considerable vitality, and may resume activity if given a chance, even after prolonged abuse. The modern physician will tell you that in most cases the best he can do for his human patient is to clear the way and give nature a chance to make the cure. In the case of grasslands that have not been completely wiped out, such seems to be the best prescription for returning them to health and vigor. Protect them against the grazing and fire which have brought about their ill health, and let what remains of the original vegetation fight it out with weeds and other aliens. There is no reason to worry about the outcome. The rest-cure will work marvels.

Weeds resemble those people who thrive best under difficulties and adversity. Prosperity and peace ruin them. They cannot retain their power under a calm and stable régime. Weeds, like red-eyed anarchists, are the symptoms, not the real cause, of a disturbed order. When the Russian thistle swept down across the western ranges, the general opinion was that it was a devouring plague, crowding in and consuming the native plants. It was no such thing. The native vegetation had already been destroyed by the plow and thronging herds—the ground was vacated and the thistles took it over. It is the same with the American prickly pear, which is regarded as an unmitigated pest in Algeria and Australia. Again, the Mormons were accused of sowing sunflower seeds along their route as they crossed the continent. The truth is the sunflowers have always been there, but the hoofs and tires of the Mormon trains broke through the turf, destroying it and giving the sunflowers their chance—a temporary one at best. No one ever saw a field protected against fire, plow, and livestock, support a permanent population of thistles, sunflowers, or any other kind of weed. Just as surely as the weeds replaced the native plants with misuse, the reverse will happen under protected conditions.

Of course this process of regeneration has its practical side. The land cannot continue to be tapped, any more than a cut-over forest can be brought back to a commercial basis if the saplings are used for fence posts as fast as they appear. A type of long-time financial policy, looking more toward ultimate than immediate profits, must be established. Particularly will this be true if sheet erosion has removed necessary mineral nutrients from the soil. In many cases the supply of phosphorus and potassium, never any too abundant, has been seriously depleted and must be restored, which involves an actual money investment. In other cases gully erosion may have proceeded to a point where some engineering is necessary to stop it. This again requires an outlay of labor, perhaps money. And whether or not money as such must be laid out in the process, the recuperating acres have to be regarded as latent, not productive, wealth, until such time as they are again ready for rational use.

What may be done about those millions of acres, particularly in the drier grasslands, whose sod has been completely destroyed by the plow, but whose continued profitable cultivation is not possible? So long as there remains the most remote possibility that these can be made to yield crops under cultivation, we may count upon human stubbornness to return, again and again, to the attack unless there is some restraint. The slightest encouragement in the form of working capital will prolong the struggle, often to the final cost both of individuals and the commonwealth. If the best interests of all concerned depend upon getting these denuded lands back into grass, what chance is there to restore them?

Under favorable conditions it has been found that the planting of such a thing as wheat-grass, and its subsequent careful protection will bring about a return of satisfactory pasture. Or if ample fields of buffalo grass are near at hand, narrow strips may be cut from them, separated into small blocks, and these transplanted at intervals onto the bare and abandoned space. With reasonable rainfall the native grass will establish itself and creep out to cover the clear intervals between the blocks. Both methods involve expense, waiting, and the hazard that drought may prevent success.

But there is a great deal of loose, sandy land, once good pasture, which has blown and drifted until it has become a temporary desert. It is vital that some cover, no matter what, be developed here without delay. Nature has furnished a hint. Throughout this region after the drought was well begun the despised Russian thistle did so well that it was often the only plant available for stock feed. Instead of seeding the area with costly grass seed, whose success is a gamble, it might be sensible to mix in a good proportion of weed seeds. If the land is abandoned weeds will be the first cover anyhow, and, as we have seen, they are transient settlers at most, preparing the way for better kinds of plants. Actually the method is not new. There is a brilliant example of its use on the bare clay slopes of the huge Ohio Conservancy dams north of Dayton, which today are held in perfect condition by a dense, well developed sod. The success of this plant cover was insured from the start by the deliberate use of the cheapest, weediest, mixtures of grass and clover seed that could be obtained. The weeds took hold at once, but their more genteel companions are now in full possession, just as the coonskin cap and leather jacket have been replaced by the fedora and business suit in the onetime wilderness beyond the Alleghenies.

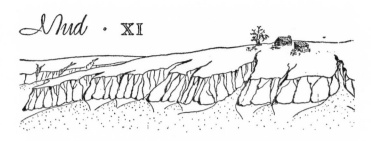

It is an early morning in March—a Monday morning, to be exact, back in good old 1913. There have been about three days of the usual spring rains, yet the air is clear and the students in the quiet little Ohio college town start for their first-hour classes as usual. But there are no classes. The streets about the gentle knoll on which the college stands are a sea of swirling, rushing, liquid mud. For three blocks on either side of the bed of the harmless trickle miscalled a river the flood is raging. Amazing, unheard-of, preposterous, but a grand show until it is seen that lives are being swept away—then paralyzing. Something has to be done, and the whole gamut of the spectacular, the futile, the utterly foolish is run, until the true leaders emerge. One of them is later to wear the twin stars of a major general, which suggests that the army is not necessarily stupid. Order is established, people put to work, and a technique for the salvage of lives and property developed on the spot.

The flood subsides. Patrols working up and down the valley, feverishly at first (they found a living baby strapped in its crib that way), and later methodically, report that rich farms have been stripped to their clay skeletons in some places, buried in a desolation of gravel in others. Within the town, cellars, streets, and near-the-river living quarters are coated with stinking slime brought from upstream in quantities no one ever thinks to calculate.

An energetic governor inaugurates engineering measures which are soundly planned to minimize destruction whenever, if ever, such a flood occurs again. The "tree cranks" of the state point out that the flood was much more severe than it would have been if more of the forests were still in place. The pious speak according to their conscience and their bile, of a "visitation of Providence" or the "wrath of the Almighty."

With variations more or less dramatic and often enough tragic, the story repeats itself, in one place after another, each year throughout the length and breadth of the land. Often, as in Ohio in 1913, it strikes without warning and finds the populace unready. Generally, however, the annual flood is taken more or less as a matter of course. The people in the lower Mississippi Valley, like villagers at the base of a volcano, become habituated to the risk they run. It is a startling experience for the visitor to New Orleans when he learns that the great river is flowing along beside the city and above it, restrained by the giant levees. And when this valley in the air becomes almost brimful it is hard to understand how his urbane hosts sleep as well at night as they do. Of course the Army Engineers are standing guard. And a great spillway has lately been constructed to divert the highest floods away from the main channel, out into the swamps which fringe the Gulf of Mexico. It may no longer be necessary to dynamite the levee far upstream, flooding out farms and villages to save the Crescent City. But the river remains a mighty thing, heedless of man.

The spectacular thing about flood is the rush of water and the threat of disaster to the lower valleys. It is natural enough then that the first efforts go into preventing of such disaster by local measures in the places most apt to suffer. The problem presents itself there to the engineer in concrete form, within a fairly small space. His energies are directed, not to preventing the coming of the water, but to handling it when it does come. If he followed it upstream, when the water comes he would find his efforts diffusing out through thousands of tributaries and eventually onto the ranches, fields, farms, and forests of the interior. Actually, of course, the flood problem begins at these sources. There is no ultimate control unless it is there. All else is palliation. But the engineer is not to be censured if he prefers to avoid all the complications which would be his if he tracked the trouble to its point of origin. In the case of the Army Engineer Corps the justification is still stronger, for this organization has no authority above the limits of navigation. The problem does not come under its wing until after it is well started. If the safety of property owners in the lower valley only were to be considered it might be fair to ask how far anyone in the upper watershed might be obliged to alter his management in the interest of flood prevention. Hope for improvement lies in the fact that these owners with whom the trouble starts should be just as much concerned as anyone. For the floods which threaten the lives and property of their fellow-citizens downstream are steadily robbing the upper reaches of wealth in the form of water and soil, neither of which can be easily spared.

To find limpid streams today one must go to the mountains or to sources fed by springs. In pioneer days the larger rivers were often clear and clean. Today they are opaque, even in quiet times of low water. At flood time, if one lowers a bucket into the Canadian, for example, and then brings it up and allows it to settle, as much as one-fourth of it may prove to be mud. If the property owner upstream could be made to realize that this mud is the same stuff for which he paid by the acre in cold cash, the flood problem would be many steps nearer solution than it is today!

The work of water in leveling the hills and carrying them to the ocean bed has gone on since the beginning of geological time and must continue to the end of it. It is a normal enough process, and certainly inevitable. The danger of the present situation is not that any new force is at work, but rather that the rate of its action has been speeded up far beyond the capacity of nature to replace the eroded soil. Consider the framework in which events are taking place. The interior of the continent is far above sea level. Most of it is more than a thousand feet, and in the western Mississippi Valley, a great deal of it much higher. In the interior the rainfall is much less than on the coast and the vegetation in consequence much sparser, affording less natural protection to the surface. Such rainfall as comes on this meager cover is apt to come infrequently, but in torrents. Moving northwest through Oklahoma, for example, from one corner to the opposite, one rises from five hundred feet to nearly five thousand feet in the space of five hundred miles, an average rise of nearly ten feet to a mile. The rainfall drops from forty inches to about fifteen a year. The vegetation changes from dense forest, with gum and cypress swamps, to short grass and scrub. The conditions for heavy erosion are perfect. The infrequent but torrential rains at the northwest exert the maximum force, yet encounter the least resistance from vegetation. The slope is relatively steep, increasing the opportunities for erosion as the water proceeds on southeast through the state. Let man enter this picture and recklessly destroy much of the protective ground cover; no prophet is needed to see what a tremendous impulse he will give to an already rapid process.

Erosion, like many another curse of humanity, grows by what it feeds upon. It behaves like compound interest. Beginning first on the exposed surface of normal soil, it first removes the sponge-like, water-holding layer of dark humus, which normally is held in place by the roots of plants and protected by their tops. Once this humus is washed away, nothing remains to absorb the water that falls thereafter. Driving along the concrete highway after a heavy rain, one sees pale patches of ground here and there which dry off almost as rapidly as the slab of road itself, while the rest of the fields remain dark and wet. These dry, light colored, almost waterproof layers are the so-called B-horizon of the soil, from which the humus-bearing, absorptive layer has been scalped by erosion. It is problem enough to have the highways, aggregating nearly one per cent of the country's area, shedding water like a duck's back into our drainage systems. But when we add the areas from which soil has been removed and which in consequence are unable to retain water, we have added enormously to the destructive power of our abnormally swollen streams. Thus does erosion promote still more erosion.

What is true of this scalping of soil—sheet erosion—is likewise true of the more familiar and spectacular type—gully erosion. Both grow by what they feed upon. As a gully cuts back, tributary gullies are cut and the damage spreads like a ringworm, in a circle. The measure of damage is not the *distance* cut back by the main gully, but the increasing *area* involved in the whole system. The more it eats the more it wants. The injury then increases, not by addition, but by multiplication—a truly frightful thing to contemplate. The end of gullying comes when badlands are formed, grotesque spires and chimneys of rock or soil standing like pegs on a board, with no stable spot where plants can grow and soil form to arrest the procession of ruin.

Gullies and badlands are the final effective protest of outraged nature, compelling the abandonment of land, and speaking their story to the dullest. But in truth they seldom appear until after the mischief has been wrought which converts fertile soil into waste. It is the quiet, generally unnoticed sheet erosion which is the true measure of deterioration over much of the United States. In the early days of the last century, and in fact until recently, the prevalent notion of soil fertility was based upon its chemical character. Without doubt, the necessary mineral elements must be present, and can be readily exhausted by unwise agricultural management. If the same crop is grown repeatedly in a field, or if the phosphorus, nitrogen, and potash are consistently sold off the farm, whether on the hoof or in bushel baskets, the soil will be depleted, unless minerals are added. But in actual practice it has quite generally happened, especially on rolling land, that more of the valuable minerals were washed away along with the surface soil in the run-off water than were ever sold off the land in the form of crops or livestock. Yet so subtly does sheet erosion do its deadly work that the steadily falling yields which have moved westward the frontier of abandoned farmlands have been generally attributed to loss of fertility caused by continued cropping alone. Just as a tree may have a rotten heart, but still look good from the outside, so may the surface of a field be unfurrowed by gullies, fair and even to look upon, yet worthless to the farmer because the best part of it has been washed off.

Equally as insidious as this quiet removal of upland soil is the fate of the lowlands when erosion starts. The level upper terraces of our old stream valleys have always furnished the choicest of farmlands, because of the abundant moisture below, the protection afforded by the valley sides, and the rich deep soil. This black soil is partly due to the greater growth of natural vegetation, partly to the gentle movement downward from the hills of much good material. But when sheet erosion begins on the surrounding upland fields this downward movement is no longer gentle. At first it actually enriches the valley, by bringing down the topsoil from above. Soon, however, this phase passes and the material brought down is the meager subsoil, which forms a pale coat on top of the fertile black valley land. Before long the infertile coat becomes so thick the plow cannot reach the dark soil buried below it and there is an immediate decrease in the yield. This process, so simple to describe and so easy to see when one is looking for it, happens in such gradual stages that the farmer himself does not really understand what is going on. He only knows that the farm has played out, top and bottom, and if he is able to do so, he gets away from it.

Great is the power of water, either for good or ill. The tumbling mountain freshets in late spring knock huge boulders about with the ease of a boy shaking a pocketful of marbles. The same stream, harnessed and regulated, will drive turbine engines with precision and speed. In placer mining the concentrated force of a small jet will strip away the side

[100]

of a mountain. The same water, spreading out gently through ditches across the barren plains at the foot of the mountains will convert them into rich green farms. Water is indispensable. What hope is there to control it in the interests of civilization?

This is not, of necessity, primarily a problem for the engineer. It is as much a matter of biology as it is of engineering. It will never be solved until the engineer and the student of plant life attack it together. The delicate, thread-like roots of plants are as vital to a solution as are mighty walls of reinforced concrete, and the black and spongy soil must play a part no less than vast reservoirs. In fact, as we have seen, the reservoirs themselves soon become useless unless the valleys which drain into them are carpeted with plant life to prevent the inwash of silt. Of course any inland pond or lake must fill up in the course of time. A foot of fill in three hundred years is not unusual under undisturbed conditions. Yet behind nearly a score of dams in the Piedmont country there has been a foot of silt added *each* year, until the reservoirs themselves have been rendered worthless in less than thirty years.

Can we check the erosion now going on? And what hope have we of restoring the enormous area at present rendered worthless by this process? Prevention, if started in time, is a cheap expedient compared with the cost of redemption after the mischief has been done. It is estimated that to prepare farmland when it is first cultivated, so that it will not suffer from erosion, entails a cost of from $1.50 to $3.00 an acre, while the engineering, fertilization, and reconstruction of average eroded land, if the damage is not beyond repair, is likely to cost not less than $15 to $20 an acre, in fact often doubling or trebling the original investment.

With a rare combination of sound scientific sense and superb showmanship, the Federal government has at length dramatized the erosion problem and made available the necessary technical information for its control.

The responsible agency that has been established is the

newly created Soil Conservation Service of the Department of Agriculture. It has been charged with the investigation, assistance, and control which belong to any effective attack upon the problem of erosion. The program which it has outlined can command the respect of the most critical. Yet we must not forget that this unit, like the Forest Service, has to operate in a democracy and cannot develop effective strength beyond that which public sympathy and support will confer upon it.

We know today that there is no one sovereign remedy, but that a combination of methods must be employed, methods which may be skilfully adjusted to the particular situation. Many of the measures are of such a character as to be highly desirable for other reasons than the immediate control of erosion itself, so that they may form part of an integrated policy of effective land utilization.

On the engineering side these measures involve the erection of barriers to check the growth of gullies where they now exist, together with the construction of series of reservoirs of all sizes at convenient places to impound the excess water which today swells the rivers in times of flood. Fields that are not level must be made so if possible, by means of terraces arranged in such a way that the water from them is not dumped out onto the public highways, but retained on cultivated ground. The highways themselves must be scientifically planned so that they do not act as stream beds in times of heavy rain. The technique of supplemental irrigation at low cost to farms in the moister, better farm areas of the country, where irrigation is today not thought of, must be developed. These are some of the problems the engineer must face.

To perfect these measures, the specialist on soils and plant life must coöperate. His task is in a sense more difficult, for it speedily involves the delicate political problem of specifying the way in which land must be utilized. He runs squarely into the ingrained American tradition that land is private property with which the owner is free to do as he pleases. Before stirring up that particular hornet's nest, let us see what should be done, rather than how it may be accomplished.

The first thing the natural scientist is likely to recommend, and the last thing as well, can be simply stated. Get vegetation back on the ground. Mother Earth is a staid and dignified old lady, no nudist by choice. Rough and broken land at the sources of streams and tributaries should be permitted to revert to forest and grassland without struggling against the handicap of plow, fire, or flock. This is only common sense, anyhow, considering our need for more timber and pasture than we have today. Increase the proportion of pasture on each farm, in particular on the rough, uneven ground which is hazardous to farm. Confine the clean-cultivated row crops as far as possible to rich, level soils not apt to be washed or blown away. Where rolling land is farmed, do not rely upon terraces alone, nor indulge in the vanity of straight furrows. Plow with the contour of the land, and on the terrace ridges use close-planted crops which form a tight, protective sod, alternating with more open crops on the level terraces themselves. When pastures are established, nurse them with the care a corporation puts into its manufacturing plant, or a banker into his (personal) investments. Gauge the size of flocks and herds, not by what the traffic will bear in good years, but on the basis of an average, wholesome, sustained yield. Practice wise rotation and diversity of crops, and see that in place of the minerals removed from the soil, a return in kind is made. These, which are, after all, strangely like the counsels of Hesiod the Greek, and Cato the Roman, are the promptings of the modern man of science. Will they too go unheeded?

Wet Deserts · XII

The true measure of the desert is not in its water, nor its sand, but in the amount and kind of its life. Deserts are not necessarily without life, sparse, hardy, and bizarre though that life may be. Fat, pulpy stems with coats of heavy wax spread their shallow roots far out near the surface, to catch such rain as comes that it may be stored against the time of drought. Insects of the desert condense the moisture of their own breath inside their impervious armor, and use the same water again and again. Seeds of countless short-lived plants lie dormant in the ground ready to spring into brief activity when opportunity comes, then relapse again into long quiescence. Seldom, indeed, is the desert lifeless, but never is the life abundant, as it is in more favored places. As to sand, it would be a hardy director who would film his sheiks anywhere save on shifting dunes. Yet Lawrence of Arabia tells us plainly enough of the stretches of rock and clay over which he fought. Again, the desert may have water, sufficient water to support rich life under other conditions. But the water may come at the wrong time of year, it may dry or run away too soon to be of use, or it may be so changed as to be unsuitable for the use of living things. Scattered over the earth are basins whose waters are so charged with salts, sometimes alkaline, often not, that life within them is a precarious matter. The plants that manage to survive look strangely like those of the drier desert, puffed up with hoarded water, gray with wax or wool to keep it in, and often standing far apart, sharing their hard conditions under a sort of armored truce. Even where the conditions are too severe for larger plants, there are forms of life, although too small for the naked eye. In hot springs not far below boiling there are tiny green plants. And in crusts of solid salt from California come thin green layers, the aggregation of living things which as individuals are invisible.

But our concern is here with deserts made by man, and not watered, but under water. For man has been as heedless with the teeming wealth in lake and stream, pond and bay, as with that of the forest and plain. Only the fact that this destruction has resulted in nothing more serious than the disappointment of sportsmen or the inconvenience of those living near these waters, together with our general ignorance of what is going on below the surface can account for our seeming indifference.

To the pioneer, as to the Indian before him, food from the inland waters was an important thing. Men of the settlements would own a seine in common and in the autumn would join to harvest fish sufficient for their winter use. These would be thrown into piles as nearly even as might be, one heap for each man or family. By lot or blindfold choice the ownership would be determined, after which the fish were taken home to be salted or smoked. Each spring-fed brook was alive with fish, while the larger rivers contained what seemed an inexhaustible supply.

Today the use of seines is unlawful, and over vast areas even the most skilful use of hook and line is ill-rewarded. Hundreds of thousands of dollars are appropriated by the government to hatch fish and restock interior waters. This enterprise is financed largely by fees exacted for those diplomas of vain hope known as fishing licenses, on the theory that the streams are empty because they have been fished out. But it is safe to say that while the fisherman has not been guiltless, he is not the real culprit.

Life within the water is a delicately balanced affair. This can be shown by sealing a live fish, a snail, and a water plant within a globe of water, placed where the sun can strike it each day. Such a little world will flourish for months, each inhabitant playing his appropriate part in maintaining the proper physical and chemical balance. The plant manufactures food from what is, to the snail and fish, waste material, and these in turn consume the food. While making the food, the plant releases oxygen, thus purifying the water so that the animals will not suffocate. Some of the waste from the fish is not in a proper form for the plant to use directly, but is made so by the snail. If the snail is left out, the little cosmos does not thrive so well, nor survive so long as it does with him present.

Within the open pond or stream the same general relations hold, but of course with many elaborations of detail. Plants of all degrees and sizes are present, and animals both large and small. Everywhere is the most intense activity, and the chain of food involves all of the organisms present. The largest fish feed upon smaller ones, these in turn upon the smallest. The smallest depend upon insect larvæ, tiny crustaceans, worms, and other minute creatures which feed directly upon the microscopic plants. The larger plants, whether rooted or floating, are also exceedingly important, in the fresh and in the partly decayed condition as well.

To maintain this system of life, sunlight is absolutely essential, for the energy from the sun is utilized by the green plants, large and small, both to manufacture the food and release the oxygen which together maintain the animals. The clearer the water, obviously the more of the sun's rays can penetrate beneath the surface on their beneficial mission. Yet steadily with the settlement of the country the water has become murkier. All of the forces which accelerate erosion have muddied the waters. The rainwater which used to be screened and filtered through layers of moss, leaves, and grass before it reached the brooks now scours into them its load of filth direct. As the surface humus has been washed away, a greater proportion of clay has gone from the subsoil into the streams, there to hang suspended after each rain like slime in a tumbler, screening out the sun for long periods with wet cloudiness. In what was probably a misguided moment the

German carp, long raised as a domestic food fish in Europe, was introduced into the waters of this country. It spread with great rapidity and flourished in the fast-muddying waters of the United States, at a time when game fish were rapidly decreasing in number. Not suited to the American palate, and more a water-hog than a game fish, it has been blamed with ruining the streams and lakes of this country. Beyond question the carp is a scavenger, eating the eggs of other fish and rooting out aquatic vegetation. Yet, like the Russian thistle in the western range, it is likely that he should be regarded as a symptom, not the real culprit. The increasing muddiness of the streams gave him his great chance, which, naturally, he took. To feed the normal population of game fish which the waters once supported, in our present muddy waters would be as easy as to feed the human beings in this country entirely from crops grown indoors, with the sun shut away by walls and roofs.

Life in the waters must have its fertilizer, just as crops which grow upon the great farms on land. In the tranquillity of nature undisturbed, this comes in the gentle drainage from the fertile soil of forest and meadow, so that the waters are rich enough in the various chemical elements that are needed for the food manufactured within them. There is a story of a small lake in one of the northern states, which yielded fabulous returns to the fishermen who lived about it. So seemingly inexhaustible was it that the villagers found it profitable to abandon their other sources of income in favor of fishing. This situation finally attracted the attention of a man who knew a great deal about water and its ways, for no lake in the region had such a record. He found the answer. The village fathers for a century past had been laid to rest on a knoll overlooking the lake and draining into it. Transformed into lime and phosphorus, nitrogen and potash, these genial old gentlemen of an earlier generation were seeping down into the calm waters below and enriching their descendants without devise or inheritance tax!

[107]

In one of the southern states a city reservoir which had enjoyed notably good water began to change chemically, and physically as well, becoming much less desirable. The reservoir lay in a huge bowl covered with native prairie. Investigation showed that instead of being pastured or mowed, the prairie was burned over frequently, thus destroying its helpful filtering action on the rainfall, and releasing an unbalanced chemical mixture, as well as undesirable sediment, into the water of the artificial lake below it. Manifestly what is good for the soil itself is good for the waters which drain off of the soil. *A watershed which is properly managed from the viewpoint of the land is the first step towards well managed streams, lakes, and reservoirs.*

Destruction of aquatic life does not end with the muddying of the water and disturbance of the nutrient balance, both largely due to faulty management. Bad as these are, industry and municipalities have made matters much worse. The waste of factories and the sewage of great cities have not only made the streams loathsome to behold and abominable to live beside, but they have put the finishing touches to the extermination of fine food and game fishes. Although it is a well established principle of law that stream pollution is an act against society, any hopeful soul who goes to work to invoke the forces of law to prevent it is likely to find his hands full. Only when the careless handling of sewage and other wastes has been a direct source of deadly pestilence does it seem possible to do much towards control.

Factory wastes very frequently contain the salts of heavy metals, particularly copper in solution. No schoolboy needs to be told that copper is poison. But sensitive as the human animal is to copper, the microscopic green plants which live in water and which are absolutely necessary to feed the fish, are infinitely more so. Less than one part in ten million will prevent their growth. This fact is often applied to keep them out of reservoirs where their presence is not desired. A sack full of copper sulphate crystals is towed around in the reservoir at infrequent intervals behind a rowboat, effectively discouraging this type of vegetation. A river which receives the waste of any factory working with metal is likely to have in it a good deal more than necessary to sterilize it against the tiny plants on which the fish are so dependent.

Both factory waste and sewage may contain a good deal of oil. Now oil is an excellent thing to kill mosquito larvæ in stagnant water, for it covers the surface and excludes the air which they need, in addition to coating them with a fatal film when they wriggle to the surface to breathe. The blanket of oil is no less effective in stifling fish by preventing the necessary interchange of gases with the air, particularly when other conditions have cut down the amount of vegetation available under water to purify the air that is below.

How about sewage itself? Containing as it does a great deal of organic material that might be used by plants and animals for their nutrition, is there any real basis for objecting to it, aside from the æsthetic one? Certainly sewage is rich and concentrated. Civilization cannot go on indefinitely without utilizing it to a much greater extent than the Western world has ever done. But when dumped into waters which do not have sufficient capacity it undergoes rapid fermentation and decay. These processes require a great deal of the oxygen so essential to the animals in the water, and release a surplus of carbon dioxide which is injurious to them. The effect is like that of great overcrowding. The sewage, so to speak, competes with the fish for the limited air supply. Additional damage probably comes from the waxy residue with which the waste finally coats the bottom of the stream bed, producing there bad biological conditions for plants and animals alike.

Through the failure of great metropolitan areas along the coast to dispose of their sewage and waste in a sanitary manner, extensive areas of oyster beds have been rendered unsafe for use. The oyster is an excellent host to the bacteria producing typhoid fever, as many people have learned to their sorrow. Wherever there is the slightest danger of contamination, therefore, the use of shellfish from the questionable area is, and should be, prohibited. The area is thereby rendered economically, if not actually, unproductive.

Although Americans eat a considerable amount of fish, and possess extensive commercial fisheries along the coast and on the Great Lakes, throughout the interior that form of food is regarded more as an accessory than as a staple. Rob an American of his coffee or tobacco and you have a rebel on your hands. Take the fish from his diet and he scarcely misses it, even though he be the worse nourished without it. As a consumer of fish the American public is decidedly apathetic. As a catcher, either professional or amateur, it is very much in earnest and has obliged public agencies to give the matter of fish culture their serious attention. We have in consequence great hatcheries which annually return to the waters countless numbers of animals. In the case of salmon such methods have enabled this unbelievable industry to continue on a machine-age basis. In mountain areas where the waters are relatively undisturbed and fishing very heavy in proportion to stream-size, the sport of fly-fishing has been kept going. In certain privately owned and regulated waters, too, there is excellent fishing, by virtue of heavy stocking and restricted catch.

Not so with the great bulk of inland fresh water, into which annually carloads of young fry are released by state fish and game departments. The returns are meager and disappointing, more often than not negligible. The trouble is not due to persistent and unlawful fishing, even though there is still today a considerable amount of illegal seining, poisoning, dynamiting, and other refined types of sportsmanship, which our haphazard system of game wardens cannot cope with. The real trouble is with the water into which the carefully reared young fish are released. Murky, unbalanced, sterile for plants as we have seen it to be, rotten with decaying waste, it is in truth a watery desert. To release millions of fingerlings into such a mess and expect them to live is a priceless absurdity. It has exactly the same logic we would find in driving a herd of yearling Shorthorns into Death Valley or pasturing them on a concrete highway. If the fish and game commissions of our several states are to be more than agencies for the useless collection and disbursement of funds they must be given authority and granted coöperation much greater than they now have. The hatching of fish, no matter how scientifically done, is but the beginning. Fish, like chorus-girls, must eat. And, as we have seen, this involves a more favorable set of conditions than agriculture, industry, and civic development have brought about in our inland waters.

If we could rob the term "fisherman's luck" of its present melancholy implications by making our streams once more wholesome and beautiful the world would be a better place than it is, both for the fisherman and those who have to live with him.

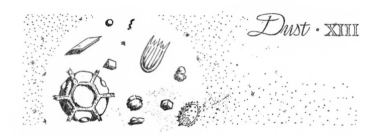

It is twenty-two years after the disastrous flood of March, 1913. The meticulous Ohio housewife, whose gentle weekly dusting had always been sufficient to keep things trim between housecleanings, suddenly finds herself unable to deal with the ubiquitous, curiously ruddy dust that is settling down out of the upper air and filtering through her tightly built establishment. She knows that dust is one of the normal tribulations of her sisters who live in the West. She had heard of the old physician in southwestern Nebraska whose diary, after his death was found to contain the following entry, "Wind forty miles an hour and hot as Hell. Two Kansas farms go by every minute." Now her radio tells her of great dust clouds in New York and Washington. The stories in the old school geography about the sandstorms of the desert had always seemed somewhat too fantastic, describing as they did the camels with their funny trapdoor nostrils and the Arab with his scarf ever ready to serve as a dust mask. Here is to-day's paper, saying that out on the Great Plains, where that red dust on her library table comes from, a child has been found stifled in a windrow of dust. And wirephotos show school children with faces veiled like little Fatimas as they trudge along the country roads out West. Pulmonary troubles, especially pneumonia, are reported on the increase because of the dust. One little town, where funerals are rare events, has four in one week and hospitals near the stricken area are having plenty to do. People are reported to be moving out with their household goods on trucks. Each day's conditions are chronicled in terms of visibility—one block, a quarter-mile, or on better days, perhaps a mile.

As the dust confuses the senses, so the welter of reports and opinion clouds the judgment. It is a reporter's paradise, an editor's purgatory. The owner of a large tract in the short-grass country, which had been plowed up for wheat, says, "We're through. It's worse than the papers say. Our fences are buried, the house hidden to the eaves, and our pasture which was kept from blowing by the grass, has been buried and is worthless now. We see what a mistake it was to plow up all that land, but it's too late to do anything about it." Others, who know the country well, say that these storms are nothing new. They have happened before. If the two-year drought could be broken, say they, the grass would start up again and all be well. The area is on its way towards becoming a vast cultural desert, like parts of western China, says one recognized expert. Others, also qualified to know, say that the actual damage is comparatively slight, the soil being mostly so rich and deep that the loss of the top means little, except on certain soil types.

A former president, traveling through the stricken region by train, is quoted as saying, "Too much of the grassland has been plowed up." And an able agronomist says the trouble is due not to plowing, but the lack of it. He blames the shallow disking, and recommends plowing the land into deep furrows, providing new ones be made as fast as the wind levels up the old. An enterprising reporter recalls the wave of indignation against a cabinet member who had once referred to the wind-ridden area as "submarginal," and who proposed moving the inhabitants elsewhere. Editors incline to play down the general serious character of the whole matter, yet not enough to discourage a liberal-handed government from coming to the rescue. A few people may be moving out of the stricken region, they admit, but the sturdy old pioneer spirit will not down—we shall all see the dusty West once more the granary of the nation, provided a little timely help is forthcoming. It is hard to tell which is the real show—the procession of news on the front page, or the kaleidoscope of opinion elsewhere in the paper.

As a matter of fact, so huge is the region within which the dust is being picked up that any particular statement may be at once true and false. Let news staffs and advertising managers wrangle, while chambers of commerce and eminent economists disagree. What if the stricken farmer has a different verdict from that of the impersonal scientist? What if one township, or one thousand, will never grow wheat again? The truth in any particular sense is only important as it fits into the larger picture. The really practical thing is not the immediately practical. To regard the dust plague as a misfortune due to the wrong kind of plow, or a chance drought, or even to concede that it is due to an unhappy shift from pasture to wheat, is to miss the point.

Unless the dust is seen as a symptom and a symbol, instead of a direct problem in itself, the misery which it has caused is of no avail. It is precisely this clever, efficient, and speedy solving of immediate problems, without regard to their general setting, which has brought us where we are. We have stretched to its limits the merely opportune. Let us not forget that the last bumper crop of wheat from the dry farming country lay beside the railroad tracks in vast heaps for months while people willing to work for food were not getting the chance to do it, and were hungry. If tomorrow some ingenious fellow were to insure that the soil of the dry West would never again be lifted into the air, it would be of no solution to the real problem which lies back of the dust storms of this year of grace, 1935.

Dust itself is nothing new. Like the circle, it is a symbol of eternal time. Long before the days of the microscope and the chemical balance it was understood that dust is the beginning and the end of all things. Dust is always in the air we breathe, an invisible world of tiny, buoyant particles, infinitely rich in its variety, and with laws of its own. While most people think of it as being only minute bits of earth stirred up by strong air currents, it contains a host of living organisms, bacteria, molds, pollen, animals, as well as fragments of material from larger plants and animals. Except perhaps in air newly washed by rain, these float about perpetually sustained by gentle drifts in the atmosphere of which the human senses are scarcely aware. Even such a giant citizen of the world of dust as the plumed dandelion fruit will remain afloat indefinitely in a breeze of not more than three miles an hour. The microscopic grains of pollen and fungus spores, capable of ascent to the stratosphere, have their own curious globular symmetry, often richly marked, but with neither right nor left, top nor bottom, as fitted to the ocean of air as the fish, the fly, the elephant may be to the respective worlds in which they live. With the rising and falling of the currents the particles of dust, living and dead, are perpetually renewed, perpetually settling out. The world of dust is never at rest, and the potential energy of the surfaces of the granules in it is enormous. One of the serious hazards of the grain-elevator business is the peril of spontaneous dust-explosion from sparks of static electricity within the dust itself. The behavior of dust is influenced by electrical conditions to a surprising extent. Dust poisons put upon plants to kill pests will not stick in place unless they bear an electrical charge of opposite sign to that of the leaf surface.

At times the dust world receives important accessions. This often happens as the result of volcanic explosions. When the great volcano on Krakateo blew up in 1883 it not only buried the entire island in a deep mantle of ash but sent clouds of it into the upper air where they hung for months, girdling the earth before they slowly settled. The eruption of Mont Pelée on the Island of Martinique in 1902 was followed by a season of voluptuous sunsets, occasioned by the impalpable dust which filled the atmosphere above North America, spreading the dying rays of light each evening into vast masses of gold and purple. Likewise, in 1912, the dust from the

Alaskan volcano Katmai spread far and high, although the heavier bulk of it dropped within a radius of one hundred miles, folding every living thing beneath a thick blanket, and apparently creating a complete desert. Presently, however, insects appeared in countless numbers, and later it was found that a good deal of plant life had managed to survive in one form or another to emerge slowly and reclothe the seeming waste. In the case of each of the three great eruptions mentioned, the succeeding year was marked by abnormally low temperatures which have been attributed to the interference of the atmospheric dust with the radiation of the sun.

While the movement of dust by the wind is usually associated with dry, treeless climates, there may be very violent activity of this sort in moister, more genial conditions. Along the shores of the Great Lakes, particularly Michigan, enormous dunes of sand were so built up. Eventually most of them were stabilized by a forest cover, but so feeble is the hold which this maintains that the slightest disturbance of the ground cover has been sufficient to start forming the huge blowouts. When the city of Gary, Indiana, was created upon the dunes the blowing sand persisted in marching through the town. Had it not been disposed of, it might have swallowed the streets just as it has the forests of pine and oak near by. When this carving of the sand is under way it forms a blast which few plants can withstand, shredding leaves and stripping off the bark, leaving trunks bare and polished on the windward side. Two kinds of plants only can resist—those which, like certain vines, can drop as the sand is scooped away below them and form fresh roots continually, and those which can grow fast enough at the top to survive burial, meanwhile forming new roots just below the rising ground line. Because the sand grains are comparatively heavy they are seldom carried far in a single flight, although they move many miles in the course of time, by repeated short jumps.

One also sees fierce, though local, dust storms on the cultivated, power-black soil of old lakes and peat bogs in the northeastern United States. Mostly these are used for clean-cultivated truck crops, such as mint, onions, or celery, and in the course of time the muck becomes very finely disintegrated. The so-called "muck-blows" which occur in high winds are not only exceedingly unpleasant, but may be disastrous to the valuable crops, particularly when they are young and tender. They also tend to injure the field itself by removal of the soil which gives it its peculiar value.

Plowed fields of any kind which are not covered during a time of high winds are apt to be blown about, even in a normally moist climate, especially if they contain much sand and silt in proportion to clay and humus. Roads, too, which in the aggregate cover a considerable area, contribute a considerable share of dust. Military men know that dust often betrays the position of marching columns at long distances, while the traditional kerchief of the cowboy had its origin as a dust mask, used on the trail behind the milling cattle.

A few decades ago, when macadamized roads of crushed limestone were being built everywhere, the white dust from them was often very troublesome in the summer months. Before many years white sweet clover, until that time an inconspicuous weed, literally swept over the countryside, particularly along the shoulders and roadsides of the macadamized "pikes." Bees thronged the heavy-scented blossoms, and pampered family horses would loaf along, greedily snatching the nutritious tops. The clover appeared because of the lime which the road dust had added to the adjacent soil, and which is so necessary to any legume if it is to thrive. The clover is gone now, replaced by more stable vegetation, but the soil is better because of its sojourn. This episode had the double benefit of attracting attention to the value of sweet clover as a crop and of emphasizing the shortage of lime in many agricultural soils of the eastern states. Similarly in Texas, exhausted and abandoned rice fields seem to recover most rapidly within the dust zone of the shell roads which pass through them.

We have said that dust is nothing new. Those who know the banks of the Missouri at Council Bluffs, or who have observed the Mississippi above Natchez, are familiar with the vertical, pale brown cliffs of material almost as fine as talcum powder. This material, known as *loess*, is found at many places in the Middle West and was dropped where it is by the wind. There are some differences of opinion as to where it came from, some holding that it was the fine flour from the glacial mill, washed out, dried and shifted by the wind, but not carried very far from the place of origin. Others think it came from far to the west. Evidently it lodged where it is because there were plants whose tops caught and held it. One can see this same sort of slow building up at many places in the grasslands today. At any rate it is a good example of the geological importance of wind as a mover of dust.

Whatever theories may be held regarding the source of this loess, there is little doubt that it was moved during very dry periods of climate, probably while the great glaciers were retreating. During such dry periods there is the least possible interference from vegetation with the lifting of soil, for deserts are at their maximum size. It is quite possible that during these very dry climatic periods the country west of the Mississippi and Missouri valleys was much barer than today, and that the westernmost vegetation heavy enough to lodge and arrest the blowing loess was located approximately where we see its deposits now. At the foot of the Medicine Bow Mountains in southeastern Wyoming there is today a huge basin ten miles long, three wide, and one hundred fifty feet deep which was certainly scooped out by the wind. Its former contents are now lying in Kansas and Nebraska, whether or not they are mingled with fine material from the melted glaciers. Elsewhere along the Rocky Mountains and within the Great Basin there is evidence enough to prove to the most skeptical how long and hard the winds have worked.

That the winds are still severe and constant enough in the interior of the continent to move an immense amount of material, no one who has been there will question. Where they have long had a free sweep at the naked surface of the earth, not much is left except coarser material that will not travel far. Such is the condition of the so-called desert pavements which we have mentioned earlier. But wherever the interior of the continent has been clothed with turf, the situation is vastly different. Here the surface material is characteristically fine, and has continually become more so through the physical and chemical processes of soil formation going on among the roots. Yet these same roots, like straw in adobe bricks, have held the fine material together against the steady sweep of untrammeled winds. The margin of control is not a large one. In the more critical areas the roots seldom get deeper than twelve or eighteen inches and the vegetation itself is none too dense. There is no saturated water table close below to entice the roots deeper and bind the soil by wetting it. The deeper one goes the drier it gets. Such is the thin, brave line of roots which holds the outposts of our productive land despite all the vicissitudes of alternating drought and favorable seasons. Properly husbanded, it is capable of yielding meanwhile a return, modest by the acre, but bountiful in the aggregate, in the form of grazing. It is no piece of maudlin sentiment to say that this frontier of vegetation deserves well of humanity.

Had we accorded it fair treatment, not even the prolonged drought of two years would have released its soil into choking, impenetrable walls, sweeping over the continent and far out to sea. The reckless overgrazing which began in 1870 and has continued since, with periodic overproduction of livestock and steady destruction of the native turf was bad enough, in all conscience. But when, from Dakota to Texas, the multiplied power and mechanical perfection of modern engineering was loosed, in competition against already struggling farmers in more favorable climates, to destroy the sod and replace it with wheat, the outcome was inevitable. This outcome was not only predictable by anyone who knew the vegetation and climate of North America, but was predicted without causing anything but resentment. With the turf gone and the cycle of moisture past its peak, with the winds maintaining their normal behavior, the country literally started to blow out of the ground. For this great catastrophe the individuals directly responsible have paid in bitter coin, and we all shall have to pay in a measure. No work of ignorance or malice is this, but the inevitable result of a system which has ever encouraged immediate efficiency without regard to ultimate consequences.

Heaven knows that flood can be frightful enough. But after all there is something tangible about water. It may wash away your property, or drown your friends, but you can see it and know how it works. You know whence it comes and whither it goes. The dust is different, today from New Mexico, tomorrow from Wyoming. It blackens the air, and hides the sun. It does not bring the sharp, quick, desperate terror of flood, but instead a slow, chilling, and pervasive horror, perhaps out of keeping with any immediate damage, but right enough in the long run.

Mile-high, these gloomy curtains of dust are the proper backdrops for the tragedy that is on the boards. The lustful march of the white race across the virgin continent, strewn with ruined forests, polluted streams, gullied fields, stained by the breaking of treaties and titanic greed, can no longer be disguised behind the camouflage which we call civilization. Yet to say this is not to be blind to the beautiful meaning, clear to the discerning eye even in the most impoverished homestead or most sordid, hopeless-seeming village of the New World. Sword and spirit never march far apart—priest and pirate—renegade and missionary—the best and the worst are in the vanguard as mankind moves along. And the general sort who move behind them are warped by the curse of the one, even as they are blessed with the light of the other.

Proverbially easy to talk about, weather and climate are correspondingly difficult to discuss with any intelligence or finality. "Only fools and newcomers try to predict the weather" runs the adage in one part of the country where, as a matter of fact, the Weather Bureau faces the most difficult technical problems in its day-to-day predictions. The visitor to Florida hears much of the rainy season, but when he tries to find out the time of year to which this refers, he gets an astonishing range of answers. An inexhaustible alibi, the weather is likewise a wonderful subject for propaganda. One recalls the hoary yarn of the farmer's anxious wife who hoped the commission locating the near-by state line would find that her home lay on the Texas side, because she understood the Oklahoma climate was terrible. In the way of general truths about the weather, none hits closer than the perennial excuse given to short-time visitors in California, "We're sorry you happened to find such an unusual run of conditions." Usual weather is like the average man, a convenient idea that is seldom encountered in reality.

While our Weather Bureau renders indispensable service to many sorts of enterprise, it is no accident that this arm of government is in the Department of Agriculture. Valuable as a knowledge of weather conditions may be to shipping, aviation, and merchandizing, it is even more so to the producer of foodstuffs. The salvage of cattle from impending blizzard, protection of tender fruits against unseasonable frosts, escape from catastrophic floods, all depend upon the possibility of at least a few hours of timely warning. And because agriculture, unlike many other enterprises, is carried on by small individual operators, government is the only agency which can supply this assistance in any practical way. Larger organizations might, if necessary, help themselves to some extent, as they do with many other technical services. This the farmers, under our present system, could not do.

Yet, with all the resources we have been able to marshal, the fact remains that it has not been possible to get to the heart of the problem which weather and climate create for the farmer. He of course needs to know in advance about the daily conditions. But even more is it essential that he know far in advance what to expect, so that his annual operations can be planned accordingly. Information of this kind is at the present in the realm of black magic and reputable agencies do not deal in that, although there is constant vigilance for any sort of clue that may make possible long-range weather forecasting. In the meantime, the patent medicine almanac and the goose-bone prophet are not constrained by any nonsense about scientific ethics, and continue to enjoy a vogue equal to that accorded the palmist and medium by our city cousins. This situation is not improved either, by the fact that in every community there are weather-wise old souls who can, on short-range predictions, often outguess the official agencies. They are like the famous bonesetter Reese, who knew nothing of scientific surgery, but who had such intuitive skill at mending broken frames that even reputable physicians were known to send their patients to him.

The great difficulty about reaching a useful working understanding of the weather and climate is in the matter of perspective. The weather of a day, a year, or a decade, is only part of the story. Just as the smooth, sharp edge of a razor resolves itself into a matter of notches and nicks, each with their own, smaller irregularities, when we look at its magnified image, so with the behavior of our atmosphere. A particular rainy day may be all-important to the man wishing to set out tomato plants, or another interested in the outcome of a particular horse race. It would be of little importance to a cattleman whose pastures depend upon the total annual rainfall and its seasonal distribution. And the rainfall for a particular year and place would not loom very large to an operator whose activities were so extensive and diversified that loss at one place or time is counterbalanced by gain at another. And for the last named, only a major, protracted shift of climate, entirely changing the aspect of a region and its cultural life, would be of decisive significance.

Climate depends upon the interaction of a great number of factors. In consequence its manifestations cannot be described by the method of individual portraiture, any more than the American people can be so described. It must be dealt with by means of statistics, and when this is done, we are rewarded by an understanding which if not complete, is at least very useful. Coming back to our razor blade, no amount of study would enable us to draw, in advance, a precise picture of the microscopic nicks which would show in a particular blade. But it would by no means be impossible to estimate in advance the size and number and average depth of them for a blade of known material and shape, sharpened by a certain process. This is the type of useful knowledge about weather and climate which we have, but we have not mastered the art of using it.

Climate has been called "the average weather," not a strictly accurate term, but helpful, perhaps. What does this involve, using the comparatively simple matter of average annual rainfall? Over a long period of years this may average, for a given place, forty inches. But the actual years with precisely forty inches, no more, no less, will be few if any. The greater proportion of years will be close to that figure, of course, with extremely wet or dry years fewer in number. There seems to be a definite tendency for the drier years to group together, likewise the wetter, but not in such an invariable way that one can say, "next year will be dry" or "three years from now we shall have very wet conditions." Even though there is evident a rough tendency for the cycle of wet and dry to complete itself about every eleven years, we can only prophesy with the wisdom of the sage, not the occult power of the sooth-sayer. We know, with the inspiration of the old Pennsylvania Dutch farmer, that "it never rains much in a wery dry time." And that no year is going to be precisely normal we may be sure. There is this much control; statistics tell us accurately the extent of the hazard in either direction which we must be prepared to run.

Now that is as much as life insurance companies have in the way of information upon which to base their very suc-cessful operation. They cannot tell a given client when and how he is going to die, but they know a great deal about the likelihood involved in this event. If many who are insured live longer than they are entitled to, enough fall short of the mark to compensate for that fact. Such is the power of prophecy conferred by statistical analysis.

How can this be of any practical use to the man who works the soil? In the first place, in making his capital invest-ment, he has in the past too often done it on the basis of bumper years. Two or even three such years may follow in succession, because of the tendency we have mentioned for years of high rainfall to occur in groups. Needless as it may seem to mention the fact that such conditions are never per-manent, the sad fact remains that countless investors have acted exactly as if they thought otherwise. Not only will the majority of years be less favorable, but years, and probably groups of them, must come when conditions will be decidedly unfavorable, even disastrous.

So long as bankers permit the farmers whom they serve to disregard these simple facts in purchasing land, this branch of industry will be in the position of an insurance company which extends protection to men of any age, figuring its premiums on the life expectancy of a man just turned twenty-one. Perhaps it is naïve to suggest that anyone who really wants to help agriculture on to solvency can do no better than shout such facts from the housetops. But it certainly would be more naïve to expect those who stand to profit by the financial vicissitudes of agriculture to give the situation much publicity. There is considerably more to scientific agriculture than the production of two blades in place of one. Almost any fool can do that when nature is with him. The goal is a system which can stand the shock of years when half a blade is all that can be had. And as a sound beginning no more hard-won capital should be involved than the inevitable turn of the cycle will justify.

Nor is this all. Civilized man ought to be less the sport and victim of the elements than he is. Good husbandry enhances the benefit of favorable years. It can, almost equally, stand as a buffer against the certain impact of unfavorable ones, and should have that in mind, as a conscious end. But it must be remembered that the two ends are not the same, and the desire for the first should be tempered by the thought of the second.

Centuries ago a royal Pharoah discussed this problem of the lean and fat years with an alert young Hebrew named Joseph. Joseph advised him to lay by the surplus of the fat years to tide over the lean. This advice is still as good as it ever was. And it must be conceded that the advances of modern technology have done their share towards this end. Vast storage facilities are now available, and methods of preparing materials to insure their long keeping. For example the discovery that wheat flour will keep fresh much longer if the germ is removed in milling has certainly not helped the nutritive properties of the flour nor its flavor when fresh, but it has made possible long shipment and a great spread of availability of this staple commodity. Canning and preserving suggest themselves at once as means toward the same end. In any criticism of the present system of private initiative, it must be borne in mind that these advances have been largely developed and made workable under that system, with tangible benefit to the whole social order. Unfortunately, private initiative has not yet suggested the means by which, in times of dearth, those who are without purchasing power can share the stored resources of rich seasons—unless we regard instalment buying as a not altogether happy gesture in that direction.

But the question of lean and fat years goes deeper than the problem of reserves and equalizing consumption. For answer here we must look, not to the good sense of a Joseph, but to the spiritual admonition: "Consider the lilies of the field, how they grow." And in truth, they have the answer we are seeking. In the prairie states there are many kinds of introduced ornamental and fruit trees, in addition to those which are native. The change from the frequently open winters to spring is a vacillating, disorderly process. Benign and lovely weather in February or March may be followed by lethal frost; growing days are interspersed between times of howling blizzard. The usual result is that the introduced plants are enticed out of their winter safety, putting forth leaves and flowers only to to have them trapped and killed when savage cold replaces balmy warmth. So usual is this that in some parts of the grassland states—where peach trees grow very well indeed, and produce excellent fruit if the blossoms are not killed—a good peach crop about once in every four or five years, or about three times in the life of the average peach tree, is the best that can be hoped for. The peach, of course, is not a native fruit.

Meanwhile, it is notable that the native plants are never roused by any false alarm of spring. Cottonwood, redbud, oak and wild plum all remain quiescent until the period of nature's caprice is past and then emerge in safety. Why and how this happens no one knows, but of the benefits of it there can be no doubt. Somehow or other in the course of an immeasurable past, nature has eliminated the unsuitable in such a way that the flora of each region is remarkably adjusted to local conditions. She may proceed with great leisure about this task. We know that oranges grew for one hundred and forty years in Georgia before they encountered a killing frost. Thereafter they were quite as dead as though they had been eliminated in the first five years. Much of man's trouble in the lean climatic years is due to the fact that he is forever attempting to grow species or varieties of plants in a climate to which they are not certainly adjusted. Particularly is this disastrous when the commitment is heavy—when all the eggs are in one basket. The remedy does not need to be labored in the telling.

Suitability of crop to the hazards of climate, then, is our first lesson from the lilies of the field. The second is no less important. Nature abhors monotony as she does idleness, unbalance, or vacuum. She clothes the native field and forest with variety, as we have seen, for example in the case of the virgin grasslands. We have observed there how the mixture of native plants possesses a resourcefulness and flexibility equal to any of the ordinary vagaries of rainfall, temperature, and evaporation. Conditions one year may favor a certain part of this mixed population; the next year a different constituency will form the favored group. However the pendulum may swing, the round of life goes on. It would be unfair to say that tillers of the soil have not utilized this principle. In the western half of the prairie states, where the threat of dryness is never far off, it has become a part of standard practice to keep at least a small acreage in the drought-resisting sorghum, or "cane," planted so thickly that the stalks are slim and spindling. Although far from a perfect ration, this can be used in place of hay if all other crops fail, and has pulled more than one farmer through the winter following a bad year. But in comparison to what should be done in the way of diversity of crops, it represents a mere gesture. The hazards of the climatic cycle cannot be minimized until a variety of crops becomes the invariable rule.

The third lesson from the lilies of the field lies in their effect upon the soil. Both they, and the animals which in undisturbed conditions eat them, return each year's surplus of new organic material to the ground, depositing on the surface minerals brought up from below, and creating humus which keeps the surface moist and mellow. Further, this surplus of litter keeps down to the utmost limit the amount of bare space and holds the ground against washing and invasion by weeds. Thus the soil itself is not only kept in the best possible physical condition to withstand unfavorable seasons, but is continually being improved. By contrast the usual result of cultivation, as we have seen, has been to produce physical and chemical deterioration, leaving the soil and the plants upon it almost defenseless in the lean years. To mine the soil persistently and trust to heavy doses of chemical fertilizer when it becomes exhausted is to disregard the plain and explicit warning of nature.

The final lesson which the seeing eye may glean from the plants of the field is that they themselves represent one of the steadiest and most certain sources of wealth, in lean years as in fat. They thrive under moderate and balanced use and are ever ready to yield their quota of material to the mower or the shepherd, providing he does not abuse this generosity. The farm or ranch with a goodly proportion of its surface still in virgin sod need not fail, whichever way the cycle of climate may swing. By disregard of this insurance on millions of acres, citizens and nation alike have brought upon themselves the dire penalties of poverty, hunger, and discouragement.

Since crops and practices must be intelligently adjusted to climate, how can we map the climates of our country to guide us in our practice? It is easy to map the separate features of climate, such as sunshine, temperature, and rainfall, but alone these tell us little. We must have a way of expressing their combined effects so that we may know how the growth of plants is affected by them. Furthermore, it is very difficult to know how refined to make our distinctions. Just as there are counties within states, so there are climates within climates. We could easily go too far for practical use. Many discouraging attempts have been made to map climate in such a way that it would be most significant in terms of native vegetation, and correspondingly, for cultivated plants. In recent years ways have been found to take account of rainfall, evaporation, temperature, and seasonal pattern so that extremely valuable maps can be made. When these maps and their meaning are well understood, it will be possible to know in advance whether great enterprises such as the extensive introduction of new crops and methods represent a sound development or a rash gamble wagered against the loaded dice of climate.

Perennially the question arises: Is the climate changing? If it is, all effort becomes a gamble, of course, unless we can predict the course of change. It is true that there are abundant evidences that climate has not been uniform throughout the whole of geological time. Plants have grown luxuriantly in what is now frozen waste near the poles, enough so to form considerable deposits of coal. At other times vast ice-caps have spread far beyond the present limits of the frozen polar regions, and the snow caps of mountains far below their present lowest levels. But is the climate changing now? To begin with we must eliminate the personal impressions of people formed during a single lifetime. There is plenty of trustworthy record to show that in such a brief space of time only the fluctuations we have already discussed can have occurred. One of the most persistent opinions, even in scientific circles, is that climate is gradually becoming drier. Before this is accepted, we must grant that the effect of human interference with natural vegetation and soil nearly always takes the form of making rainfall less efficient, and of introducing the weeds characteristic of drier climates than those in point. For example, burning and overgrazing encourage the cactus to move in in place of grass, and grass to come in in place of trees.

In terms of centuries, there is more reason to believe that greater fluctuations have taken place. For example, the wine grape cannot today be grown as far north in Europe as formerly, and we know with great certainty that parts of Scandinavia, Japan, and North America once covered with hardwood forests such as oak and beech are now occupied by the cooler types of evergreen such as spruce and fir. Without

[129]

going into great detail, it seems evident that the climate of the northern hemisphere is very gradually getting cooler, but at such an imperceptible rate that present lives and existing institutions are not likely to be affected. Although we call the present climate postglacial, it actually is behaving more like an interglacial period, and may indeed, in the course of some thousands of years, prove to be so. In the meantime, for all practical purposes, the chief changes of climate which need to concern the human race are those reversible fluctuations, in terms of whose average we express the character of our surroundings.

And herein lies the really vital contribution to planned economy which can be made by the science of climate and weather. Interesting as it would be to envision the climatic shifts of the next few thousand years, and important as it is to have daily forecasts, the real need is to impress upon the popular and official mind the fact that variation is the rule and not the exception. Yet it is equally important to understand that this variation between wet and dry, hot and cold, forms a reasonably orderly pattern to which human enterprise can and must be adjusted.

Once the character and extent of the inevitable fluctuations are appreciated, climatic hazard ceases to be the irrational thing which it is at present. Not until then will it be possible for land utilization to be elevated from blind and futile makeshift to a reasoned and orderly policy.

XV · *Pests*

Injurious insects, say the experts, have thus far had the advantage in their warfare with mankind for the food supply of the world. No matter what devices of poison or biological strategy may be devised, it seems to be impossible to stop the persistent surge of the half-million or better species of insects. Man is a single species standing, it is true, at the apex of the animal kingdom so far as intelligence is concerned. But the insects for their part probably represent the culmination of another line, specialized in various ways, and particularly in their capacity for increase. One is reminded of the French army officer, during the darkest days of World War I, who sighed with relief when he heard that China had joined the Allies: "Of course the Chinese have no great trained army; but remember, enough rabbits can smother a lion." At every step in the production of useful material from the soil, our ravenous rivals take their toll—with an aggregate which annually reaches a staggering sum.

Nor are insects our only rivals for the organic material which we need. Rodents and other destructive animals, as well as microscopic plants which cause disease and decay, are unbelievably greedy. A hundred rabbits eat as much as one cow, if not more. Weeds, while manufacturing their own food, do so at the expense of space, sunlight, and water which are needed by useful plants. The annual water requirement of a sunflower plant is at least equal to that of the corn plant growing in the row—all too often beside it. And since much of our foodstuff must depend on rain which falls before the growing season begins, we may see how little there is to waste. In the

[131]

grain belt, as the roots of either weeds or crops grow downward, they progressively dry out the soil from the top down. Only in unusual seasons do the summer rains really renew what has been stored and then removed. All along the line it is war to the knife.

The chronicle of this unceasing battle is one of absorbing interest, no matter whether one can understand the technical details, or whether he is simply interested in the adventurous angle of it. A Frenchman, spraying his grapes with blue vitriol to sicken thieving boys, finds that the fruit is unharmed by disease which ruins his neighbors' crops, and thus invents the first fungicide. French peasants use Ku Klux Klan methods and by direct action destroy the government hedges of barberry, which, they say, are blasting their wheat with rust. The government, thus moved to secure scientific counsel, finds that the peasants are right and the hundred years' war against the rust begins. California citrus groves are threatened by scale insects which secrete a poison-proof coat of wax, beneath which they suck the juice of the plant with impunity. The lady-beetle is found to be exceedingly fond of scale insects and is marshaled into an army which does the work as neatly and completely as any mercenaries ever served a royal crown. The Japanese beetle which is making devastation in lawns and gardens through the East, is discovered to have a fatal weakness for geraniol, the scented material in rose geranium. Traps are baited with the substance and the beetle succumbs.[1] Small wonder then, that no matter how other learned disciplines may suffer, the study of insects and plant diseases has been subsidized by state and nation with a lavish hand. And with the same ingenious resource in the face of immediate emergency that has always distinguished the American people, each new challenge has been met. Yet we have the somber verdict with which this chapter begins: The fight, to date, has been a losing one. What is wrong?

[1] Sad to say, this neat trick has not lived up to expectations (1947).

Perhaps some illustrations will help us answer this question. On the western range there are numerous rodents, including jackrabbits, which feed upon plant life just as cattle or buffalo do. Their aggregate consumption of pasture is of course enormous, and has led to very active measures to reduce their number by poison, traps, and other methods. The theory has been that they destroy the pasture and make it less valuable for herds of cattle. But when studies are made of the actual distribution of rodents in natural grassland, it is discovered that the number does not become significantly large until after the grassland has been more heavily grazed by cattle than it should be. From that point on the turf suffers from the combined destruction of domestic and wild animals. The serious character of the rodent plague is actually the result of disturbed conditions brought about by human interference. If the range were not overloaded beyond its capacity to produce compensating new growth, the rodents would remain in equilibrium with the rest of nature and not, normally, constitute a serious pest.

We have heard much of the plague of grasshoppers, crossing the country like a wave of devastation and consuming every green thing in their path. Yet a fence of three barbed strands of wire has been known to stop them. In the Wichita National Forest is such a fence. On one side the herbage is heavily populated with various types of destructive grasshoppers. On the other side the species present are somewhat different, and the number very much less. Actually, of course, the fence served to prevent overgrazing. But the truly surprising thing is that the hungry pests did not occur to serious degree on the side with the large amount of potential food. Like scavengers and trouble-makers who have no place in an ordered existence, they found their opportunity only after the natural balance had been practically destroyed. Thus, when man begins the downward course of destruction, does nature operate to accelerate the dizzy process. As the damage increases so does the possibility of further damage.

Another simple illustration is of interest. There is a borer which has been very destructive to the elms, girdling the bark and causing the death of limbs, often of the whole tree. Why has not this insect long since exterminated its host? If we examine the damaged trees, we generally find them growing in exposed and sunlit places. In the shadow of a building or a clump of other trees there is little if any injury. In nature elms come up in the shade of cottonwoods and willows, often in the company of young maples and ash trees. Under such conditions the borer does not thrive, but must depend upon those venturesome or unfortunate elms which risk their lives outside the proper sphere. Man's fondness for the elm as a shade tree of course multiplies the number which are growing in unsuitable conditions; indeed, they are often put where any tree short of a scrub oak or cactus would be lucky to survive.

It is well known that maize does not thrive commercially much north of the Canadian boundary, nor wheat too close to the Mexican line. The former is essentially a warm climate plant, the latter one of cooler regions. It has been found that both are much more susceptible to disease when grown near the limits of their temperature preference than when grown safely within that range. And in general any plant or animal far from its proper home must have unusually favorable conditions to reach a healthy maturity.

The examples given illustrate one point: that parasites and predators, while a constant menace, are never completely successful in their destructive efforts under what we shall call normal conditions. Undoubtedly there have been instances of such complete success, but only at the price of extermination of the victimized plant or animal—an eventuality which can have had only one outcome for the destroyer. The earth is peopled by organisms which have been through such fiery test for an unimaginable length of time. Hosts and parasites have survived only because they have developed the ability to live together.

It is an old and tried rule in biology that when a form is

transplanted into a new locality to which it is adapted, it is likely to spread with astonishing rapidity because of the absence of competition and its accustomed enemies. There are many familiar illustrations of this ranging from the English sparrow and starling in North America to the rabbit and cactus in Australia. Probably the red man exhibited the same sort of a rapid population increase when he entered our continent, and certainly the white man has done so. European crops such as wheat, brought to this country, have behaved the same way under the protection and intentional encouragement of man, and so have the various American plants which were taken back to Europe, particularly the potato and maize. We know, of course, nothing as to how these invasions operated before the time of man's appearance, and particularly before he had developed to the point at which he became an important, conscious factor.

So far as we can tell, however, the invaders, whether plant or animal, are eventually compelled to slow down. If nothing else stops them, competition with their own kind will do it. The period of unrestricted increase ends and the newcomer subsides to his proper place in the picture. Just what this place will be depends upon many circumstances. In the case of the English sparrow the change in domestic architecture away from Victorian gingerbread to the stark simplicity of modernism has certainly affected the abundance of nesting sites. Better care of garbage and other waste, and the supplanting of the horse by the automobile have restricted the opportunities for feeding in the cities and towns. This bird, once described as an incorrigible, dirty gamin of the streets has now become rural, and has had to go back to the farm to live on shocked and shattered grain which the shiftlessness of many farmers provides. The European starling with its noise and filth has not hesitated to desecrate even the capitol of the nation, arousing the ire of others who wish to be heard in that forum, and defying the onslaught of those responsible for the maintenance of order and calm. Gas, water, and alarms all seemed to be ineffectual to do anything but provide copy for the newspapers. The bird likes it here and apparently intends to remain. But in the spring of 1935, interesting to report, huge numbers of them were found dead from some cause or other. Whatever the factor may be, it may be expected to check the hitherto riotous propagation of this offensive alien. And it is certain to be assisted by other checks as time goes on, perhaps even by new strategy from our fellow-scientists in Washington, until the starling sinks to its rightful place in the avian population.

Man himself is by no means immune to this rule which operates upon the successful invader. The red Indian, although he had developed remarkable centers of culture in Mexico, Central and South America, and had spread over the rest of the New World, did not by any means have a dense population. It is unnecessary to try to enumerate all of the influences which operated to limit his numbers, and indeed many of them we cannot know. But we are certain that he had serious technical limitations in the matter of tools and available power, and enough is known of the history of the Mexican civilizations to know that competition with his own kind was at times a potent, even a decisive factor. In fact, so delicately balanced was the adjustment within this comparatively sparse population that the pressure caused by the earliest white settlements on the Atlantic coast seems to have been transmitted to the interior, causing serious displacements there long before the first explorers had visited that part of the continent.

White man with his superior technical resources has been more successful, if numbers are a measure of success. But epidemics and wars have killed their millions, while famine has stalked the land, not overtly, but in the invisible cloak of malnutrition and prolonged underfeeding. The Civil War between the states is not to be measured alone in terms of lives and property destroyed, but also in terms of the spiritual discouragement which for nearly two generations thereafter clouded the once proud South. Energy and hopefulness, no less than the capacity for numerical increase, are essential to mankind. And these were destroyed in the southern states to a degree which few people in the North have realized.

So far as numerical increase among the whites is concerned, we have already seen how remarkably it is being retarded. The great period of population expansion seems definitely to have passed its crest and the day of stability is probably not far off. When that time comes the human race in North America will have gone a long distance towards becoming part of a balanced system. The struggle will be simplified in one respect at least: pressure on our natural resources will be stabilized, excepting insofar as the unpredictable human mind may conceive new needs and the spirit foster new desires over and beyond the means of subsistence.

Man, of course, has become the sponsor of a biological experiment without known parallel in the history of the earth and its inhabitants. He is the first example of a single species to become predominant over the rest. Heretofore there have been great groups of species—invertebrates, fishes, reptiles, and finally mammals—each in their turn replacing those which had gone before and becoming the conspicuous, characteristic type upon the earth. As these newer and more successful ones appeared, the less efficient and older either became extinct or were relegated to a place where they did not suffer from more efficient competition. The reptiles of today are a modest and innocuous lot compared with those gigantic forms which once roamed, and claimed, the earth. But never, so far as we know, has a single kind so completely swept all others aside and taken possession as has mankind.

Furthermore, man has not only become predominant, but as the price of his power, indeed of his survival, has assumed conscious, deliberate control. He has established a new order, with his own good as the criterion of it. He is attempting to rule the earth as a god might do, not only seeking what he needs, but manipulating all that is about him, supplying the conditions of life for the lower organisms which he uses, and combating those which are hostile with resources they do not have. He no longer accepts, as living creatures before him have done, the pattern in which he finds himself, but has destroyed that pattern and from the wreck is attempting to create a new one. That of course is cataclysmic revolution. We have seen something of what this entails in the way of hazards and failures. Soil has been exhausted or depleted, forests and grasslands destroyed, topography injured, and conditions produced which facilitate the activities of these pests which compete with man for survival. Man is not ignorant of these consequences, but as an individual he acts as though he were. So vast is his empire, and so numerous his brethren, that no one feels, in any convincing sense, that his personal activities can constitute a serious menace in any but an immediate, direct, and personal way. So long as consequences of such measure are avoided, the individual takes little heed. The gift of intelligence with which mankind is endowed represents the collective effect of individual intelligence, acting in the main on problems of expediency. What develops in the way of policy seems the blind resultant of these innumerable integers.

The past century has witnessed some rather heroic efforts to break this fatal chain. In particular wealth and science have been employed to combat the enemies and limitations under which man labors in pursuit of his daily bread. Engineering skill has devoted itself, often cumbrously and ineffectively, but in the main successfully, to relieving him of toil. He has delved deep into the mysteries of other organisms, with the object of utilizing or destroying them. There has been no stint of money for science, where the practical end could be demonstrated to legislator or philanthropist. Apart from the empirical wisdom which peasant tillers of the soil possess, and which has in Mennonite and Czech colony more than once proved itself, it is safe to say that we have today, not all the knowledge we need, but a great deal more than we use. That is to say, that if what knowledge we possess were consistently applied in the tilling of the soil and the management of range and forest, the course of waste and destruction, exploitation and loss, would be arrested. Could that be done, the possibility of an ultimate equilibrium favorable to man would be immeasurably advanced.

It is needless to ask why this knowledge is not consistently applied. It is not, of course, uniformly diffused. Even if it were, it would not be effective as it should. Character and self-discipline, the training that comes through apprenticeship, are all too often lacking in the individuals who, having the knowledge, must be entrusted with its application. This is the answer to those who cry for research and education. Both are good; both are essential. But they are not good enough. In all his study of the pests and predators which handicap him, man has not taken sufficient account of the chief, which is himself. It is the human element in practice which is deficient. One may acquaint a young man with all there is to be known about sound practice, but if in his early youth he has not been taught habits of responsibility, persistence, and industry, it is a waste of time. *It is not merely soil, nor plant, nor animal, nor weather which we need to know better, but chiefly man himself.*

The Way Through

In all their rule and strictest tie of their order, there was but this one clause to be observed: *Do what thou wilt.* With those four words the wise old Benedictine, Dr. Rabelais, sums the law which governed the inhabitants of the beautiful Abbey of Thélème. Free, enlightened, noble of spirit, they dwelt in the midst of plenty. Untouched by fear or need, no one of their number could find the occasion of his own good in the ill of another. "Men that are free, well-born, well-bred, and conversant in honest companies, have naturally an instinct and spur that prompteth them unto virtuous actions, and withdraws them from vice, which is called honor. Those same men, when . . . . brought under and kept down, turn aside from that noble disposition . . . ; for it is agreeable to the nature of man to long after things forbidden, and to desire that which is denied. By this liberty they entered into a very laudable emulation, to do all of them what they saw did please one."

Thus wisdom plans the perfect state, and the sensitive artist portrays it. In the older dreams all that remained was for the all-powerful benevolent despot to establish it. In reality, of course, wisdom far too often faltered, art yielded to the fleshpots or to despair, and monarchs were not benevolent. In the modern world there is more to be considered. Science and technology have entered the picture, affecting the course of events at every turn. The mass of mankind must be won before they can be guided, and rare is the man who can win them without recourse to devious means.

The United States of North America today is no man's Utopia. Yet if ever man set out to establish a realm of earthly heavens he did so on this continent. Until the time of its settlement, the idea that man could progress from a worse state to a better was never taken very seriously, at least not so far as this life was concerned. In the wisdom of the ancient East there was no place for such a notion. Change might occur, of course, but it was the remorseless and hopeless change of a huge wheel on an axis which never moved forward—eternally turning, but never advancing. North America was settled in the fresh bright morning, after the Western world had shaken itself awake from the long, immensely invigorating sleep of the Middle Ages. Hope and unbounded faith, crude and selfish though their personal manifestations might be, were abroad. The New World was, in vision, a better world. It makes no difference what craft or sordid resource individuals may have used to gain their ends, the fact is that the migrant throng had one genuine, vital idea—that of progress.

As each new homestead was established and each new community took form, there was little reverence for the past as a guide. In essence, each new center was to be better than the old, and its children happier and better than their parents. The real motto was not the four words above our coat of arms but the four words of the founder of the Abbey of Thélème: *Do what thou wilt.* Like the Abbey, each new haven was richly dowered. There was enough for all.

With the slate thus clear, rational beings might be expected to have made provision, not alone for an equitable distribution according to immediate needs, but for permanent, just and stable returns in the time to come. Yet as we have seen, the prizes were snatched with little regard for others, and none for the future. A curious blindness this, in a world that professed to be looking ahead.

This is not to deny that there were sages and dreamers, as well as statesmen, who worked at the shaping of our country. Franklin and Paine saw the evils of concentrated wealth, and the former inveighed endlessly against waste, which has been our besetting sin. But their hands were forced by the magic of those two words, "liberty" and "equality." Liberty became license, and equality chaos, with the disastrous results we have been at some trouble to explain in the preceding chapters.

It has been our task, by repeated and insistent emphasis, to show the unbalance which man has produced on this continent. And it should be clear by now that this situation is a very dangerous one. Unbalance creates further unbalance, and destruction of the means of subsistence proceeds at an accelerated pace. The picture we have seen is not one of utilization and adjustment, but rather one of exploitation and waste. We have seen how vast stretches of natural vegetation have been looked upon as obstacles to humanity, and destroyed, when in fact they are not only essential as a safeguard to the normal occupations of agriculture and industry, but could have been in themselves an unfailing source of steady, dependable wealth. All of this, having been brought about under what has appeared to be a system of private ownership and initiative, is now being cited as a powerful and convincing argument against the continuation of the system.

It is possible to be resigned to the situation. Destructive change is a part of the normal work of nature. If it is going on much faster than usual, what of it? Matters may be depended upon to right themselves ultimately. The mere fact that white humanity in North America has tremendously accelerated the natural cycle of erosion and change, and completely altered the pattern of life on that continent, impoverishing it as a habitat, is of no more importance in the physical cosmos than the fact that during the Permian period the earth was cold and dry. Vast glaciers and perhaps vaster deserts in that age made it impossible for the rich flora of tree ferns and their kind to survive. The tougher conifers weathered through, and still retain possession of the colder, drier, forest regions, augmented elsewhere by the wealth of flowering plants that have arisen since and established themselves. If we render barren any considerable areas, we shall of course be obliged to vacate them. In that case the very absence of animal life will afford the necessary condition for their recuperation, however slow. If a large part of the continent becomes unfit to support a population, that population will abandon it, until it can recuperate. Why be so concerned about the morrow?

The trouble with this viewpoint is that people, unlike horses, will not stay in a burning building if they can help it. Nor, in their haste to escape, are they likely to be orderly. Once safely out, they are neither very ceremonious and logical in establishing blame for the fire, nor particularly gentle in their treatment of the culprit, real or supposed, when they lay hands on him.

Easy as it may be to foresee the wrath with which future generations will witness their squandered heritage, there does not appear to be much active resentment over the waste of our natural resources at present. Texas is much less concerned about the future oil supply of the United States than she is lest Oklahoma or Louisiana be permitted to drill faster than she. The man who pays exorbitantly for the wood to build a kitchen shelf views the problem in a very immediate way, as does the farmer who cannot meet his rent or taxes because of depleted soil. There is resentment in plenty, but it is directed at persons and institutions rather than actual causes.

Democracy and the right of private property are two very different things, yet they are inseparably associated in the American mind. They are, moreover, the two institutions which just now are in grave danger. There are, of course, many things in life that are more important than either, but both are the result of prolonged struggle and development. If they are to be cast aside, it should not be for any idle reason.

Their position in the present instance is especially weak because it has been through their perversion that the common wealth has been dissipated for the benefit of the few, rather than conserved for the good of all. If people enjoying the privilege of democracy cannot be entrusted with the stewardship of their resources, what could be more sensible, or more humane, than to place them under a benevolent dictator, as the fascists advocated? Or if the powerful persist in robbing the weak, and exploiting them by political and economic means, why not sweep away the whole mess and turn to communism? These are important questions in many minds today.

If we believe that art and manners are prophetic, there is certainly not much ahead. But it is possible that these manifestations represent the fruit of a period that is passing, rather than the germ of what is to come.

Our modern art, and certainly our behavior, is increasingly episodic. Nothing is acted or depicted as though it were related in time, place or consequence to anything else. Each moment is regarded as an atomic entity, an independent, final thing in itself. We hide away, not for periods of spiritual ripening and repose, but to be something which we are not. There is chaos bewildering, and sadder than the slow spinning of the web of tragic fate. In the latter, at least there was order, cause and effect, such as sober experience and intuition insist upon. Yet the very fever to crowd as much into life as we do betrays the significance of passing time and the power of human choice, even in matters of no importance. The modern world with a curious inconsistency lets no man forget that time is the stuff of which life is made.

Were one, from a cool and distant vantage, to devise the symbolism of the era we have been passing through, nothing more perfect could be thought of than our manners, our pictures, or our music. Small wonder then that the two political philosophies which have been most vocal are but different facets of the same principle of order through violence, looking toward eventual calm through perversion of the understanding. Each alike contains the canker of its own destruction, for each involves the suppression of individual personality by means of individual force of leadership. Yet in each is an element of consistency and coherence which we cannot boast.

We have developed through the ostensible encouragement

of private initiative and responsibility. The beneficiaries of this system are now fighting with their backs to the wall against governmental paternalism. They do not know, or will not concede, that it is paternalism which has made them. William the Conqueror did not parcel out the Saxon holdings with any more lavish hand to his retainers than our government distributed those of the Indians. The Norman king made his awards on the basis of services rendered, and imposed conditions of tenure and responsibility which eventually made the English landed class acutely conscious of its duty to society. We have passed out titles of ownership without assigning obligations in the same measure, and without regard to the final good of all. The paternalism was that of a weak and indulgent parent, moved by present clamor rather than by any sense of future results. It is the children of just such parents who have to be restrained with violence—at the expense of society—when they become adults.

It is unnecessary to go into the unpleasant evidence of our general lawlessness. In large measure this lawlessness may be attributed to freedom without a strong code of responsibility. Curiously enough, this is combined with a powerful sense of order and organization whenever practical necessity arises, as our industrial and business advances show. If revolution ever comes, it will be the result of the insistence for order, no matter how disorderly the means adopted to secure it.

There is food for serious thought in the fact that the two most vigorous political movements of recent decades have risen to power as a result of this demand. The failure of the old Czarist régime was due less to its severity than to its essential disorder. Anyone who doubts that need only refresh his memory concerning the condition and morale of the Russian fleet in the Japanese War, or look into the equipment and training of the huge armies which Russia sent to their doom in the World War. The specter of communism has no terrors for an ordered community.

As for fascism, it is an application of martial law to the

body politic when disaster threatens because of confusion. In shipwreck or panic or riot, as in battle, it is idle to talk of individual liberty. Salvation depends upon discipline and command, and in time of disorder, intelligent people insist on both. To believe that this country can defend its institutions from either communism or fascism by persecution and propaganda is simply a piece of blind stupidity. Nor could any mistake be graver than to under-estimate the strength, the intelligence or the moral earnestness which motivate those who advocate the destruction of our present institutions. They are not to be stopped by bullets, either of lead or gold. Our only defense is to set our house in order, if we think it worth saving.

We have a philosophy of individual initiative and freedom, confused by emphasis on equality. In our wholly laudable desire to do away with the injustices and privilege of the Old World, we have flown in the face of common sense. Science, as well as practical experience, offers abundant proof that men are far from equal in any measurable respect. By our denial of this patent fact we have a nation in which men are less equal before the law than they are today in England, against whose social order we rose in protest. The strong among us, without wasting any effort to demand the external trappings of power, have proceeded to appropriate that power, at the expense of the common good. And as a result, they are free from much of the acknowledged responsibility which should accompany power. They are like the bootlegger, who makes his profits without being a recognized member of commercial life, as was the legitimate liquor merchant. If the latter did not live up to his obligations, it was not because his identity and place of business were not on record.

It must be admitted that those who have profited most under the present system have not displayed the most brilliant generalship during their periods of greatest power. The unrestricted mergers of great industries, which form a perfect precondition for state socialism, were arranged under conservative recent administrations, as were those breaches of corporate trust which have inflamed the popular mind and which ended by making the government the mortgagee of a tremendous amount of property. Stupidity, where it handles its own case, has a fool for a client.

As we look over the story of nature, spreading alive before our eyes today, or narrowing back through the long vista of geological time, we see no toleration for structures or organizations which ill fit the work they have to do. Cumbrous reptile and bizarre cycad are alike swept out of the stream of life. Can we expect better for an unseemly and unbalanced social order?

We have had the institution of private property, supposedly, and it is that institution which is now being assailed from many sides. Is it not possible that the trouble has not been with private ownership as such, but with the fact that it has not seriously and consistently been the rule in this country? The abuses of our forest resources and our grazing lands were not essentially the ruination by individuals of what actually belonged to them. Rather they were due to the irresponsible exploitation of concessions and leases of the public domain, granted to private enterprise by government under conditions of economic advantage such as no business concern would even consider granting to another. No matter what justification political philosophy may have offered, the bargains made by government were unfair to the public it represented, and have had ultimate consequences even more unfair. To grant the right of pillage and exploitation and then blame the results onto a system of private ownership with individual initiative is neither just nor straight thinking.

Somehow the thought will not down that both democracy and private ownership deserve to be tried under better conditions than they have yet enjoyed in this country. It is hardly too much to say that we have never had either, in the strictest and best sense. We have said that the exploitation of forest and range is not a chronicle of legitimate private ownership which failed, but of privileged concession or lease of property which belonged to others, often to the public. Even the system of homesteads by which much of the public domain was settled has hardly been a fair trial of private ownership. The size of the allotments has not always been wisely proportioned to peculiar conditions of climate and use. As we have seen, a family might starve to death in the grazing country on a farm of one square mile, while a quarter or even an eighth of that would mean comparative comfort in the beautiful valley of Virginia.

Large irrigation projects have been developed with a system of payments and fees which made the whole enterprise seem very businesslike. But when, because of market and transportation problems, these projects have failed to prosper, people who would never welsh on a personal debt have pressed the government to postpone or remit the moneys due it. Such examples hardly represent normal cases of private ownership, or offer a clear test of the system.

In many places the system of farm finance has obliged the farmer to water his investment to the same relative scale as those of the ill-scented corporations which have been so frequently and profitably bankrupted. No matter if the deed (secured by heavy mortgage) be in the farmer's name, his luckless venture does not represent what he could do with a fair, clean start at private ownership of his farm, under a reasonable system of taxation.

We are on the eve of a determined movement to increase greatly the property held and administered by government. This will in many cases entail the payment of substantial prices in public money to owners whose original title was cheaply obtained, and who have, in the meantime, depleted the value of their holdings. It is reasonable to expect that the burden of these, as of other costly governmental enterprises, will fall most heavily upon the middle classes, already reeling from the successive blows of war and depression. It is axiomatic that political and social stability rests with the middle classes. There is of course the question of whether the innovations will benefit those who pay for them, but there is also the more serious question as to how much more this group can bear, without a disastrous disintegration at the lower fringe. If it becomes impossible for people of good capacity to prosper in our system, it is too much to hope that their talents will not be lent to help destroy that system.

The publicly owned forests and other enterprises in the more stable socialistic countries of Europe certainly afford a tempting instance of what can be done. And our smartly managed army, coast guard, and mint show what government control can do in our own land. Our school system is essentially a socialistic enterprise. To a degree these bright examples are shadowed by the dark facts of bureaucratic jealousies, undoubted waste, and chronic political interference. We shall have to make the choice.

One fact certainly must be granted. It is human nature for a man to take better care of his own property than of another's, providing he has been trained to do so. People living in rented houses are decidedly slower about shutting the windows in a rainstorm than those who live in their own. There should be no inconsistency in managing private property in such a way that it will yield a steady, dependable return and at the same time serve the permanent interests of society.

Perhaps the most potent argument for government expropriation of property at this time is to be found in the fact that resources are being wasted which the commonwealth requires for its future survival. The direct test as to whether this carries weight is the government's will to step in and condemn properties which now are, and in the future will be highly profitable. Oil and other mineral resources, so essential to modern civilization, and now being squandered with a bestial prodigality, are nationalized upon their discovery in Denmark. Would that be possible here? How about the best of our uncut forests now in private hands? What of the choicest range lands, and, to be thoroughly consistent, good farming lands? These represent assets which are worth conserving for the good of all, and if we may judge by experience, there is little guarantee that they will be conserved. From the standpoint of practical politics no one believes that government will go in seriously for the ownership of such resources, unless we have a revolution. But if there is continued insistence for government ownership, it is most likely to take the form of an anæmic policy of accepting white elephants. Thus will the policy of an unwise and indulgent paternalism be preserved—at the cost of dissipated public wealth.

So far as the attainment of democracy goes, it is a problem of many facets, of which we may only touch the few that most concern us here. The worst obstacle is the despair of the individual at ever making his one voice heard among so many millions. Perhaps the remedy lies in placing more, not less, actual responsibility on the smaller units of government, while simplifying the purely political machinery of the larger. The situation was stated well enough by an inscrutable President who said that it was essential for small units to decide matters for themselves but equally essential that in many matters they all decide to do the same thing!

Not only must the individual feel less futile in the scheme of things than he does at present, but, if democracy is to succeed, it must see that he is better informed. In fact, informing him is one of the best ways to make him feel a little less like a nonentity. Only in slippery business is it necessary to keep others in the dark—"the eye of the evil-doer waiteth for twilight."

Needless to say, in giving people information, the best of all ways is to catch them young. A southern banker tells of passing a farmhouse, neatly kept and obviously prosperous. To his intense surprise he saw ensconced upon the front steps an old duffer who was chronically inefficient, notoriously a failure. Stopping to make inquiry, he learned that the place was being handled by the children, trained in 4-H clubs sponsored by the government. Livestock was in excellent condition and of good breed. The garden was well kept, the cellar well stocked. In every respect the place was self-sustaining, and there was, perhaps for the first time in generations, a growing surplus of cash.

If this were an isolated incident, it would not be worth the telling. But it is typical of the situation in thousands of families. By voluntary associations, sponsored by trained and sympathetic workers, a substitute for the old system of apprenticeship has been introduced into American life. There is perhaps no more hopeful sign on the horizon at present than this, yet in far too many communities resources and encouragement are needed to further such work. If the financial and political energy which goes into propaganda of discontent were turned into 4-H channels it would do no harm.

But the old must be informed as well as the young. Often this is a gesture of piety, but perhaps not so often as many suppose, particularly if the information is made interesting and turns out to be dependable. It is true that an extension lecture on poultry-raising is likely to get a slim crowd if there is a good medicine show in town the same night; in such case the wise lecturer will adjourn and observe his rival's technique.

The governments have made greater efforts toward informing adults who handle the soil than toward any other single vocational group, excepting their own employees. It would be erroneous to regard the present crisis as due to a failure of this system of information. Rather, it is one thing which has mitigated and delayed the crisis.

Necessarily, the first efforts at diffusing popular information were halting and tentative. Many of the earlier bulletins, for example, are not worth the paper they were printed upon. Scientific knowledge as applied to agriculture is a very complex matter, constantly growing, and still far from its goal. Many of the state agricultural agencies were seriously handicapped by politics in the earlier years, and some still are. Public departments interested in agriculture carry a tremendous load of routine duties, and are constantly being called upon to solve emergency problems. One of the best soil specialists in the country, for example, is kept so busy with trivialities that he has little time or energy to devote to thought and experiment along permanently significant lines. Even today there is in many places distinct pressure upon scientific staffs for frequent, rather than excellent publication.

In consequence a great deal of the information handed out is of the nature of that found in a cookbook—useful enough for preparing a meal, but of no account in the intelligent planning of diet. Even the present campaign to enlighten farmers on soil conservation has been possible, not as a matter of foresight and policy, but because the problem has become so acute in many places that it constitutes a direct emergency.

If a farmer consults his county agent or experiment station today with respect to controlling certain insect pests, the chances are he will be advised to clean up his fence rows, grubbing out the shrubs and burning the weeds. As an immediate solution, this is good. But the end results may be quite otherwise. The fence row is likely to be the last stand of the native plants and animals, including the game birds which are the farmer's best defense, in the long run, against his insect enemies. Or let us suppose a farmer in the drier grassland province contemplates the growing of wheat. He is counseled with regard to the plowing, planting, and cropping technique peculiar to dry farming, perhaps even warned that he cannot expect frequent crops. But of the cycles of the weather and their inevitable ruinous effects he must learn by bitter experience.

There is, in other words, too much emphasis on detail, not enough on policy. Counsel and advice might very well deal with the problems of the individual as they extend over space and time. It would be interesting to observe the effect of more emphasis placed upon community welfare and the results in the generations to come. Such methods are of course too slow for the apostle of direct action, but they might make needless his plan of throwing democracy into the discard.

With a new generation trained in the efficient stewardship

of private property, and the older counseled from a rich fund of growing scientific knowledge, emphasizing constantly the importance of policy and management on a permanent basis, the problem of taxation still remains. Intricate and vexatious, it ramifies into all branches of economic, political, and social life, reaching far beyond the realm of applied biology we have been traversing. Probably its adjustment will never be equitable and harmonious. Too many debatable matters are involved. There is little agreement on principles, and less on practice. Yet it is clear that the first obligation of the citizen is to support himself and his dependents. That alone constitutes the discharge of a duty to the state, and no tax is just which moves a family below the line of self-subsistence. Again, there is in this country a constant tendency to penalize by taxation any initiative shown in the management of property. This operates directly and inevitably against any sound policy of conserving resources in the interest of sustained return.

It would even seem possible for government to encourage good management and effectively discourage management which works against the public interest. Taxation is a powerful instrument, for other purposes besides the raising of revenue. In the past it has too often operated to discourage good management rather than bad. The man who improves his property in ways that can bring him no immediate return is likely to be reminded of his folly at the next assessment. The man whose property deteriorates suffers no penalty; indeed, he often escapes the tax increase which comes to the better citizen.

Thus does government at the present time join with those insistent forces which focus our attention upon the need for immediate advantage rather than future good. In this insistence upon present profit at any cost, rather than in the institution of private ownership as such, arise most of the troubles we have been considering.

Let us suppose that the policy of taxation could be altered

so that the widest exemptions are granted to the owner whose management is self-sustaining and whose property is well conserved. Suppose that stiff rates were imposed upon those properties whose value is being dissipated by lack of proper management. The combination of incentive with penalty is powerful. The man who behaves like a trustee for the future will have a more tangible reward than the title of "master farmer." The landlord who holds an acreage for speculation and allows both tenant and land to run downhill for lack of intelligent supervision would be brought up with a jerk.

Such a policy would go far to clear up that confusion of thought whereby the immediate is considered practical, the future theoretical and, by implication, contemptible. And in the end it could be certainly counted on to increase the national wealth, and by that means, the public income. It is not even too much to hope that tenant farming would be greatly decreased or else elevated from its present degradation, if the mismanagement which it usually presents were taxed out of existence.

The present demand to tax out of existence fortunes and enterprises beyond a certain size may be wise and necessary, or it may prove disastrous. But it would seem, on the face of things, to be a less immediate need than the use of taxation to encourage conservation.

Finally, the obligation of taxes is perennial, and they must be paid in money. Market conditions may be such that produce from the land cannot be converted into cash. At present no mechanism exists by which taxes, as in primitive life, may be paid in kind. Yet during the periods of depression, when there is no market, the government becomes an extensive handler of produce, in order to feed the unemployed. So we witness elaborate schemes for beating the devil about the stump, the farmer going into debt to pay his taxes in cash—if he is able to borrow the money; the government in turn using the money to buy and distribute foodstuffs and other essentials. On occasion we might relieve the struggle to invent new devices of government by turning back and learning from those who practiced simpler ways of living.

There is no escape from the fact that such a program as we have pictured, essentially moderate though it be, faces tremendous obstacles in the accomplishment. But we are far past the time when affairs can be trusted to run upon their own inertia. We have had enough of blind driving.

For the perspective of the newborn, which knows no planes of distance, we must substitute that of the mature, with its sense of continuity and proportion. We are not an insensible people, utterly brutish, concerned solely with today, and incapable of thinking about tomorrow. But we need to remind ourselves, in our quest for immediate subsistence and wealth, that while a bird in the hand is worth two in the bush, birds breed in pairs and nest in bushes.

Science has the power to illuminate, but not to solve, the deeper problems of mankind. For always after knowledge come choice and action, both of them intensely personal and individual. Science is like those services which supply a battle commander with information of the enemy and technical advice on physical problems, but which cannot relieve him of the task of decision. For the last his own intuition, perhaps even the toss of a coin, must serve. The inescapable character of this dilemma is recognized in the old military maxim that action on an inferior decision is far better than no action at all.

We have received, without professional language, the verdict of science upon an impersonal matter—the unbalance between man and his surroundings. In the chapter just preceding we have suggested that the institution of private ownership deserves further trial, or perhaps better, a genuine trial, before it is discarded as a means to achieve that order which is essential to the welfare of the human race. But we must bear in mind that science, as such, affords us no sanctions. It may inform us with regard to any particular social or economic system, but it cannot make our decisions for us.

The automobile, X ray, and the conscious use of vitamins are so recent that most of us cannot fail to realize the difference in life which science and technology have brought about. Advertising agencies find themselves obliged to borrow the trappings and the jargon of science, if not its solid truths, in order to inspire confidence in their displays. The microscopes which they picture may be out of joint and blind, and the "noted authorities" whom they quote may be cheap mercenaries, but it all seems to help sell the commodities. Modern science began with the wizards and necromancers of the Middle Ages, and is still invested with the awe which surrounded them. Even the scientist entering the laboratory of a specialist in another field is obliged to pinch himself now and then.

Indeed, the faith which reposes in the human mind for the power of science to work miracles is at once touching and dangerous. It is a curious destiny to befall that branch of knowledge which has done most to free mankind from its cruder superstitions. And because the faith is not groundless, it becomes very important for everyone to understand just how far it should go. There are probably things which science cannot do, as well as many which it can. The scientist himself has to work in a very human way, as those who look to him for help should appreciate better than they seem to.

If science is magic, then magic is a very simple thing. The man of science examines the thing in which he is interested thoroughly and often, until he is completely sure about it, and then invites his fellows to do the same thing, to be doubly sure. Touch, taste, hearing, and smell, as well as sight, all aid him in his examination. If he encounters something which, like the other side of the moon, is beyond the reach of his senses, he had to do like the rest of us: guess about it. His only advantage in guessing is that he probably is better acquainted with that part of the moon which all can see.

Sometimes, but by no means always, the man of science can control the thing he is examining, and thus learn its behavior under special circumstances. This he calls an experiment. Often he is obliged to take apart whatever it is he is learning about. This he calls analysis. If the thing is fairly simple, he can put it back together, as a child might do with a block puzzle. The chemist often does this in synthesizing compounds. But if the thing is very complex, like a living animal or plant, the scientist is more helpless about putting it back together than a six-year-old with the kitchen clock.

[157]

Which means that each still has a great deal to learn about the thing whose parts are strewn about him.

What is true of the simplest plant or animal is infinitely more true of man and of society. The delicate interplay of motives, the clash of desires, and the seemingly spontaneous growth of culture patterns, so like the irresistible, rhythmic process of birth—all of these involve matters which defy the relatively simple language of science, even when science affixes names to them!

This is not to say that the study of human behavior or of society is a futile occupation. On the contrary, it is highly important. But it does suggest that social control, unlike chemical manipulation, is still, and may always remain, far from being a matter of formulæ and routine. Thus, when the scientist has suggestions to offer for the good of mankind, the business of getting them adopted ceases to be a scientific matter, and enters the realm of art.

The artist who undertakes to manipulate society—often, it is true, somewhat like a farmer boy manipulating a runaway calf—is the politician. The medium in which he works is that most evasive, at once most pliable, resilient, and difficult of all —human nature. It does not follow that there is anything essentially ignoble in his task, as many so wrongly believe. Certainly he has the courage to attempt a manly enterprise. And if he fails, or if the technique which he is obliged to use is not always edifying, perhaps it is less his fault than that of those who should stand at his shoulder with their counsel, their scrutiny, and their support.

In this modern world, where neither height nor depth allows us to escape from conditions brought about by science and technology, no group of citizens is under heavier obligation to assist the man of politics than are the scientists. Yet they cannot, as some fondly suppose, and certainly should not, take over his task. How then, can they best serve?

One does not need to read the tracts of the Chemical Foundation or the utterances of those priests who have gathered themselves about the altar of relativity to know that each discipline considers itself to be particularly potent. Biology, with whose applications we are here concerned, is no exception.

With this—we hope—saving smile at our own earnestness, it may be suggested that, apart from its obvious service to the art of medicine and certain aid in the more immediate problems of agriculture, biology has scarcely tapped the resources which it holds for social use. The fault is on both sides. Society, with a few honorable exceptions, has not seriously underwritten the work of the biologist in the United States. If the young man with a flair for biology wished to become financially secure, he has been obliged to go into medicine, or some vocation in which he could afford science as a hobby. To a limited extent the government service has afforded security of tenure, with retirement pay; but here the scope of research has been necessarily restricted and the better men rapidly drained off into administrative work. There remains the teaching profession. Here the number of posts which give the incumbent the leisure and the facilities needed for creative work are relatively few, and not too often recruited from less favored places. In these latter, which comprise most of the teaching posts, the really tragic loss to society has come not from overwork and underpay, bad as these are, so much as from isolation, discouragement, and lack of stimulus to the men so isolated.

It would surprise most laymen to know that Russia, Japan, Italy, Germany, and even Great Britain are far ahead of us in their employment of science in the public good. The end of the World War left this country without a superior in the fields of scientific endeavor. The American scientist traveling in Europe was accorded the respect due one who comes from a center of his calling. The old attitude of patronage was gone. But we have not held on to our advantage. When budgets have had to be trimmed, the laboratories were the first to suffer. The universities, where, after all, a great deal of the world's best research has been done, have saddled their investigators with routine duties to an extent undreamed of in the Old World. Many of the best have had to accept deanships or directorships in order to receive a wage commensurate with their training and the standard of living expected of them. Even the generous allotment made by government for unemployment relief and placed at the disposal of scientific departments could not be used efficiently because the trained have not had time to direct the untrained properly. Society, like the individual purchaser, in the long run will get just about what it pays for.

In comparison with some of the newer governments of the Old World we still have some cause for thanks, it is true. Our men of science are not constrained to bolster up an ideology with their findings. Science, religion, and government still preserve their respective identities. The fountain of knowledge still runs pure at the source, though its flow may be checked by a false sense of values among those who should give it generous support.

On the other hand, success is its own best explanation, and the workers in science are not blameless. Too many have lost the vision, permitting themselves to be swamped in needless routine, or have devoted their energies to angling for relatively well-paid administrative jobs. And among those who have achieved professional distinction by their original work, it is the honorable exception who has taken pains to explain to the man on the street what he is trying to do. Yet the greatest have never been ashamed to do this—Huxley and Faraday lectured to workmen, Timiriazeff to peasants.

There are of course great investigators who lack the skill to interpret their own work. It is likely, however, that many more lack the desire to do so. Their attitude is that of the inveterate golfer or chess-player towards his sport—the game is the affair of no one but himself and others equally competent. But only in the laboratory does the man of science have the right to lock out others. His findings once made belong to the world, and his is the charge to make them known. Perhaps if the scientist were given, not less of technical training, but a great deal more of liberal training than he usually gets, it would make him more directly useful to the rest of us than he frequently is. Effective publication, no less than investigation, is an obligation which rests upon the man of science.

Indeed, there is much for the scientist to learn if he plays his part in the game. He can hardly afford to let it be thought that his word is for sale, as it too often seems to be in the case of expert witnesses. There is little doubt that if scientific societies set out to change this practice they could do so. The federal courts have shown the way, by securing their own scientific commissions when questions of fact are to be determined, instead of allowing each side to hire its own witnesses. Scientific groups sometimes put forth exaggerated claims in order to secure financial support. This can end in only one way—by the destruction of confidence. The wealth of the scientist, no less than that of the soldier, is honor.

Finally, if the advice of the individual scientist (and we speak here principally of biologists) is to be worth following, he must fight off the effects which specialization has on him as an individual, without sacrificing his status as a specialist. He must develop and maintain a catholic viewpoint of his field, which in point of fact he seldom has. The battle for recognition of new disciplines did not end with Pasteur's triumphant vindication of bacteriology. It is still in full swing, as anyone who knows the intimate history of biology in America must admit. Illustrations could be multiplied, but the one most germane to our purpose will suffice.

Since 1900 the United States has moved to the forefront in the study of the relation of plant and animal to their environment. This subject, which is natural history in a new guise, has been called *ecology*. It treats of the relation between the individual living thing and the atmosphere and soil about it, and of course the relations which exist between and among living things.

To the ecologist a landscape presents a great deal more

than its technical details, such as the names of plants or the physical texture of the soil. Rather, it appears as a totality, with each factor, so far as possible, considered in relation to the others. His work involves analysis, of course, but only as a means to final synthesis and interpretation. *When he enters a forest or a meadow he sees not merely what is there, but what is happening there.* To him, then, there is afforded a glimpse of continuity, integration, and destiny which is indispensable to management and control in any real sense.

The preceding chapters have been, speaking broadly, an attempt to interpret the relations and adjustments of man as they appear to the ecologist, with due regard for the many intangibles which enter the human setting. If these chapters have told their story, the importance of ecology to plant and animal industry, and to any program of land utilization, should be obvious.

Notwithstanding this fact, a number of great universities do not recognize this discipline, or pay it lip-service at best. What is still more serious, the various state experiment stations, even in predominantly agricultural states, have been very slow to add trained ecologists to their staffs. Happily the Forest Service early received recruits with adequate ecological training and their influence has been increasingly apparent. But in Great Britain the ecologists are being consulted at every step in planning the proper utilization of those parts of the Empire not yet settled, thus definitely ending the era of haphazard exploitation. There are hopeful, but all too few signs that our own national government realizes the part which ecology must play in a permanent program.

So vast and diverse, however, are the conditions which any program must encounter, that it should gather its strength from every part of the country. Neither the ecologist nor anyone else can render advice without information. His problem, in a peculiar sense, lies "in the grass roots." There are probably few counties in the nation in which, over a period of years, a resident ecologist would not yield heavy returns. Certainly in many counties income from lands now rendered worthless by erosion would have sufficed to support such an adviser, as surely as the people on them could support their family physician before the farms went out beneath their feet.

We take it as a matter of course that a city of fifteen or twenty thousand should employ a chemist, even though many do not. At one time such a suggestion would have seemed absurd. The proposal for a local ecologist is a parallel. There are counties, to be sure, in which the situation could be met, providing that the county agent had at least a measure of ecological training which today he seldom has. But in general the duties of the county agent are so insistent and immediate that they should be supplemented by, not combined with, those of the ecologist.

While the county agent instructs his patrons in the more practical problems which they encounter—handling of live-stock and crops, marketing, and farm engineering—the ecologist should devote his energy to study and his thought to the future. Thus would he supplement the work of his colleague and furnish the sustaining background of policy which, as we have seen, is too often lacking in the daily strain of meeting problems directly.

From the studies of the local ecologist, whether he serves one county or a group of them, must come the data indispensable to state and national planning. And from his discourse with farmers and business men we might expect that local measures would frequently take their start, thus lessening the burden of responsibility upon the higher units of government. Indeed such measures would go toward preventing ultimate, perhaps violent, interference in the lives of citizens from those higher sources.

The ecologist, with all of his professional training, should be chosen with some regard for his talents as a publicist. People no less than plants and animals are a part of his material. He should of necessity have the equipment to work with them, comprehend their problems, and admit them to his own

[163]

confidence, for unless the general citizenry catch an understanding of the whole scene of which they are part, they will not be fitted to participate in a solution of their own problems. And upon their capacity to do so, if honestly and well informed, are free institutions predicated.

Dust storms obscuring the sun for days at a time were raging when the author began writing *Deserts on the March;* today, as the author concludes what has been to him an interesting adventure in applying science to our living problems, rain is falling and has been falling in the greatest quantity since the weather records began, swelling rivers into murky torrents laden with rich farm soil. Before his eyes in the short space in which he has written, the inevitable turn of climate has swung the cycle away from the menace of drought to the danger of flood. Everywhere about him he has seen the landscape as unprepared to withstand the one extreme as the other, thanks to the unconsidered destruction wrought by our haphazard ways.

Within a few months nature has run the scale of her seemingly inconsistent behavior. With rare perfection she has displayed the limits of her caprice. No plainer or clearer warning can we ask. The fields which last year were parched, are now gutted. Yet the few remaining prairies and forests are today alive with the beauty of rich growth, even as last year they stood through the withering drought with sturdy vigor.

Surely it should be clear that the grassland and the forest must be restored and protected to an extent not yet dreamed of, not for reasons of sentiment, but because they represent sources of certain return under all conditions. And to the balance which they display must man look for his soundest lessons in the construction of his fields to be buffered against whatever may come.

Only with the works of his hands thus attuned to the compelling frame of soil and climate will destructive change take its proper place as a dim memory of the hideous thing it is.

Deserts in Retreat · XVIII

Twelve years have passed since the preceding chapters were first printed. Since then, a score of excellent books have been written about the resources which have made this nation great and about our obligation to conserve them. At least sixty millions of acres have, with the technical supervision of the Soil Conservation Service, been put under proper land use and management, halting erosion and restoring lost fertility. The care of millions of additional acres has been influenced for the better by our growing consciousness of danger. These measures have not only arrested damage—they have contributed vastly to farm prosperity and to the feeding of the world during its present distress. The estimated increase in production on land so safeguarded is at least 20 per cent.

The land restored has included a generous portion of the high plains which in 1935 had been devastated by wind erosion. The financial cost of this particular restoration was about one dollar an acre, but the decisive factor was not financial. It was the determination of communities of men in Texas, Oklahoma, and other western states to collaborate on the solution of a common problem.

Since the beginning of the century there have been increasing numbers of societies devoted to the conservation of particular resources. These have included groups of sportsmen and lovers of trees, birds, wild flowers, water, and more recently, of the soil. At first each group pressed for a solution of its individual problem, mostly by the passage of laws that were merely temporary expedients.

Typical was the breeding of countless fish to be released in waters which civilization had rendered unfit to sustain them—as though, by some sort of biological mass action, the fish might come to overwhelm the metallic poisons and biological filth from cities and the silt from eroded farms which continued meanwhile to pour unabated into the arteries of our landscape.

Here too the past decade has witnessed a quiet but profound change. Each group, following its problem to the source, has bumped into the others—as explorers working up the fingers of a delta must ultimately meet at the parent stream. You cannot have fish without an abundance of clean water. You cannot have water, either for fisheries or industrial use, without forests and well-managed farms which will regulate the flow of water after it falls. You cannot have an adequate supply of timber without an intelligent program of land use. Wildlife must have suitable conditions in which to live and breed. Game animals, songbirds and wild flowers require areas of native vegetation—whether forest, grass, or desert—not required for other use. To feed and clothe itself, and certainly to engage in world commerce, this nation must protect its soil from destruction by wind and water. (We can thank a forthright Southerner, Bob Montgomery, of Texas, for telling the southern planters that every bale of cotton traded abroad for gold has cost them one hundred and thirty tons of soil carried out to the Gulf of Mexico.)

Today, while the secretariat of each of the several conservation groups still retains its pride of accomplishment, all of them are working together as never before. They, and the members who stand back of them, sense that the problem is manifold only in its symptoms. In essence it is one. That essence can be stated simply: All renewable natural resources are linked into a common pattern of relationship. We can save any one of them only by measures which save them all. And we are a part of the whole which must be conserved.

This is sound science and an intensely practical matter. We have been deceived by the glib statement that science has given man control over nature. What does it mean, for example, to say that a rider controls his horse? Bit, whip, and spur, however valuable, are accessories—useful in proportion to the self-discipline, the judgment and understanding of the rider. The latter must know horses in general and his own mount as an individual. Then horse and rider become a system, and the fabled Centaur symbolized that fact.

We do not and cannot manipulate nature from the outside. We must work our will by knowing laws and conforming to them, never forgetting that we are a part of that upon which we work, as horse and rider are interrelated. Our bodies are composed of the elements of earth and air, and every breath we draw is an interchange of those materials. The work we do is an expression of the energy of the sun, fixed into foods by plant life, perhaps elaborated into new forms by animals. We are not independent of the forces of nature—at best interdependent, at worst, pathetically dependent. The marvelous perfection of the internal combustion engines which draw a giant bomber through the skies is possible only because their designers have known and scrupulously respected the orderly budget of energy and material transformation.

These laws which serve us so well in the mechanical realm apply quite as rigorously to landscape. They are simple in principle. They suggest the rules of accounting, upon which business is built. Whether you are dealing with money, or water, or minerals, or energy in the form of the products of plants and animals, you can take what is there, no more. An ordered landscape, farm-wide or nation-wide, is not a tap to be left open and drained as fast and completely as we please. It must be rather a system, sturdy yet in delicate balance, so managed as to have reserves against the great cyclic swing of need and less favorable conditions.

It is quite as possible for the scientist to assay the budget of a landscape as it is for an examiner to determine the condition of a bank, or for a physician to determine whether a human body is gaining or losing in its struggle to survive. It is a matter of cold science, which no amount of political ranting or shallow enterprise can settle one way or another, any more than respectability can save a bank or love alone can stay the hand of Death.

Even so, the scientist has to guard himself, for he is human and has his predilections. Engineers and biologists, for example, speak a very different language. Excepting agricultural engineers, very few of these highly trained specialists have any understanding of the laws which govern living things and systems, such as the soil, of which they are a part. Even if courses in biology were included in their schools, we could not be certain that they would remedy the deficiency, for many biologists are too concerned with evolution and what has been called "the deadly grammar of the dead cat" to consider the interrelations of living nature here and now. On the other hand, working biologists in the field—foresters, public health specialists, soil conservators—see so much of the damage wrought by industrialism gone wild that they are impatient with the needs of our technological society.

The result is that when the two groups view a problem such as the growing water shortage in the industrial eastern states, they do not see eye to eye. The engineer is inclined to blame fluctuating rainfall, to rely upon man-made devices, and to absolve industry and urban development. The biologist, conscious of the fact that the control of water begins where it falls, sees his answer in our interference with the balance of nature. This divergence of view is evident, too, in the problem of controlling the Mississippi and other areas of flood hazard. It is plain that these two groups of public servants must hammer away at each other until they reach a mutual understanding before they can enlist the efforts of laymen.

Can the essential qualities of balance, order, and reserve which exist in nature be maintained under human dominance? For western civilization as a whole, the case remains to be proved. It is technically possible; the real problem is moral. One of the most profitable experiences of the past decade has been the chance to see, here and there, communities which have done reasonably well in establishing a permanent relationship with the land. These include most of the Amish and Mennonite communities and numerous other settlements of continental European origin. They generally combine the ancient peasant traditions of stewardship with common religious bonds. This certainly makes sense; obligation to the land is fundamentally a matter of faith, and coöperation has the quality of spiritual fellowship.

Many of these groups are feeling the strain of an alien industrial culture about them. Children rebel against traditional ways and their elders show increasing signs of emotional stress. Thus it is that, for our secular world, the great proving ground of the Tennessee Valley may have more to offer. It is a unit, but not an island. It seems to be absorbing the industrial age, using it without being overwhelmed by it. Perhaps the most encouraging side light on the TVA is the fact that it is warmly defended by Southerners of conservative temperament and that the attacks on it seem to come chiefly from those who would obtain political advantage by wrecking it. If it lives up to its beginnings, it will demonstrate collaboration between the local community and government at its best, with the individual keeping his self-respect and initiative.

I have said that the moral problem of conservation is far more serious than the technical. I am using the word moral in its broad and ancient sense, as including anything that involves human choice. There are signs of increasing will toward protection of our resources. Granting that this exists, the problem of political action remains to be solved, and it seems just now to center about the relationship between central government, the local community, and the individual —a problem so well on its way toward solution in the Tennessee Valley.

Elsewhere the situation is less happy. The average farmer, upon whom falls the custody of all of our arable land and no small share of our other resources, is confused and resentful. He is overworked at present, but that is offset by his increased income. His complaint is against government, which seems curious, since he has never before had one which has tried to do so much for him. His dissatisfaction is not a product of war, for it has been growing in volume for a quarter of a century. He wants his relations with government simplified and wants to do as much for himself as he can.

Farm prosperity is good conservation. Where a man's treasure is, there his heart will be, and generally speaking, the landscape begins to wear away at the fringes of prosperity. Government solicitude for farm distress is much more than expedient politics, it is sound statesmanship. In the dark days of 1933 the urgent problem seemed to be to get more money into the farmer's hands. Destruction of surplus was not a happy solution. Seafarers do not enjoy the jettisoning of valuable cargo from a distressed vessel. Such measures are emergency actions. The government did get money to the farmer, while reducing the apparent surplus; but destruction went against his convictions and those of the Supreme Court, too. The result was a wiser measure, combining farm subsidy with better care of the soil. This is the present Agricultural Adjustment Administration, the most gigantic effort at agricultural reform in our history and with one exception, in world history. The worst thing about it, in broad principle, is the thing which makes it tick—paying the farmer to do what he generally ought to do for selfish reasons. There is a better way, but it takes courage, patience, faith, and skill. It is the method of those leaders who strive to make people desire their own betterment until they themselves begin to work for it, and who, when the people then request counsel, are ready with the wisest counsel that can be given. This is the essence of enlightened democracy, as against the doctrine, however benevolent, of regulation.

The surpluses of farm products which caused depressed farm income has been obtained not by farming, but by mining the soil. Especially hurtful were the three great cash crops, corn, tobacco, and cotton, each a major source of farmland erosion along its clean-tilled rows. A farm, to be balanced somewhat as a natural landscape is balanced, ought to have a fair proportion of legumes and meadow, and often native vegetation such as woodlot or prairie. Moreover, its layout should be planned.

Again, in a great industrial country like our own, where the urban population exceeds the rural, the production of essential food and fiber cannot be left to happy chance and the farmer's best guess. The fabric of our economy is too tightly interwoven for that. A growing season is very different from an assembly line. The economy of a factory can be shifted in a few weeks or months; that of a farm requires a cycle of years, usually four or five. Some way has to be found to apportion each farmer his task, within reason.

During the Hoover administration a brief attempt had been made to issue up-to-the-minute information regarding supply and demand to the farm public in the hope that, under free enterprise, this would guide the farmer in apportioning his fields to various uses. It was the sort of inside information which lies behind the daily market quotations. Perhaps it went too far inside—at any rate there was pressure by selfish interests on the government and the service was promptly throttled down for slow and sedate release after it had ceased to be news and had become history.

Later, farm relief was started. It began with a single barrel and ended as a battery. Committees elected in each county studied the farms in that county, on the ground and from aerial photographs, trying to work out the scientific use of each field in the light of the nation's needs and the permanent welfare of the soil. This activity was guided by state land-grant experts working with Washington, but the actual work was local. By a combination of rewards and penalties, the county committees urged farmers to fall in line. Compulsion, however benign, does not please the rural American.

Meanwhile, other factors have added to the farmer's confusion. In earlier days his friendly government, with its magnificent technical services, was personified to him by the county agent, working out from the land-grant college of his state. The quiet labors of these agents were slowly moving in the direction of better land use and management, through education and demonstration. The county agent still remains a separate agency, overworked as ever, yet vital contacts between government and farmer have been routed past and around him.

In places where the soil erosion problem was critical, farmers have organized soil conservation districts which make available to them directly the help of the Soil Conservation Service. These districts have worked well, hampered only by the shortage of technically trained supervisors. Here again is a contact between government and farmer, wise in its intent and beneficial in its effects on the land; yet paralleling, if not duplicating the others which have been mentioned. No wonder the farmer is puzzled, at times morose, or even rebellious. Nor did it add to his peace of mind when the War Food Administration was taken from the hands of the Secretary of Agriculture, who is in fact the man responsible for food production in our country.

The government cannot stay out of farming, any more than the farmer can stay out of government. The bond is primordial. Civilized government is as truly a farm product as corn meal. It was not until farming made possible cheap and abundant food that men had energy to spare to become civilized. The technical knowledge needed for farming is biological knowledge, based upon intricate, costly, and prolonged research which only a government can sustain. The needs of a civilized country for food and raw materials are too serious a matter to be left to chance. The farmer needs the government and the government needs the farmer.

Yet it would be folly to suppose that the farmer and the government can work out salvation by themselves. The men and women who live in cities and towns and who now compose the majority of our population are involved quite as deeply, if less directly. Their good will and understanding is necessary to the farmer's stewardship. Their food supplies and industrial raw materials are at stake, likewise a respectable proportion of their investments. Urban owners have title to much of our cropland, in amounts varying from a quarter to more than half of it in different states of the Union. In Oklahoma there are more than 200,000 farms. About 60 per cent of them are owned by individuals who do not live upon them and whose responsibility should be inescapable.

Tenancy of itself need not be an evil thing, providing it represents a partnership and not a system for exploiting land and tenant. Doubtless more landowners are guilty of inattention to business than of greed, for if gain be the object, the sure road to it is the prosperity of the tenant and the care of the land. No matter how hard the tenant works, he must have back of him the capital, the collaboration, and frequently the inducements to treat the land as though it were his own. The basis of relations between owner and tenant is the lease. Leases ought to be so framed that the tenant will have assurance of tenure if he is to do his part. They ought to provide for a fair sharing of both hazard and advantage, and they ought to insure the tenant a living from the farm, regardless of financial ups and downs. Leases should provide, too, for reasonable facilities and improvements so that the tenant may do his work without lost motion and may be housed adequately. They should embody a plan for operation that will conserve the soil and minimize risk—framed not in terms of single years but of the cycles of years which are involved in any intelligent system of land use and management. The reform which would strike most directly at abuse of the soil in the states where it is worst, would certainly attack the present haphazard relationship of tenant and urban landlord.

There remains a threat more subtle than the palpable disorder of neglected tenant farm operations. It is not confined to marginal land where erosion is most obvious and spectacular; nor to absentee-owned farms. On the contrary, it involves the best of our farm land and many of our most prosperous farmers. It is sheet erosion, the slow removal of thin layers of surface soil—a loss whose effects can, for a long time, be palliated by energetic tillage, rotation, and use of fertilizer. It is a danger augmented by the fact that the good, thrifty, hard-working farmers on whose land it is occurring can scarcely be convinced that anything is wrong.

This situation exists particularly in the north central and northeastern states, where the bedrock is covered by a thick mantle of glacial drift. When the topsoil is gone, there still remains weathered mineral substance that can be plowed and worked. In the prairie states, which have between three and five feet of rich black topsoil, conditions are still more deceptive, or there may be no color change to show that many inches have been lost.

Much of our fine farmland is gently rolling or so slightly sloping that it appears level and seemingly immune to erosion, thus further adding to the farmer's false sense af security. This is true in the rich Black Swamp Area of northwestern Ohio. Yet the rains of late winter carry out from here sufficient farm soil to muddy Lake Erie half way to Put-in-Bay and the cumulative effects of this silt have all but ruined the spawning grounds of the more desirable species of fish.

The operators of our richest general farming areas must realize that soil loss is not something for hill folk alone to worry about. Frequently the remedy is very simple, and profitable, too. On my own Ohio farm we have merely changed the old rectangular fields into forms that fit the topography. We now plow parallel to the river which runs through the farm and are saving, not only our soil and fertilizer, but the water which we need to keep on the ridge tops. The benefit to our crops was obvious at the end of the first growing season.

Under our system there probably will always be questions as to authority and responsibility. How are these to be divided between central and local government, between government and private agencies? The answers, in most instances will come from an actual showing of results, rather than from political disputation. Whatever local government and individual enterprise will do superbly well is not likely to be taken out of their hands by federal agencies. Whatever they neglect is likely to be lost to them.

This is just what is happening with respect to local banks and farm finance. The purchase, rehabilitation, and equipment of farms requires long-time loans at a lower rate of interest than banks have cared to offer. As a result the government entered the field, borrowing money from the banks at a still lower interest rate! Again many farm loans require careful supervision of and advice to the farmers who need to be set on their feet. Many banks have been unwilling to go to this trouble and expense, even though their accumulated deposits go begging for borrowers.

It is idle to talk of private enterprise unless men are enterprising. Banking organizations and individual banks here and there realize the possibilities of mutual benefit to farm and bank wherever the latter measures up to its opportunity. The finest traditions of American banking are built upon "character" loans and the friendly, responsibile interest of the banker in his community and in his client's business. Now that chain stores are widespread and finance themselves, the rural banker finds much less opportunity to employ his resources in making loans to local merchants. His logical outlet today is outward from his village or town into the modern type of scientific, scrupulously managed family farm. If he prepares himself for it (and it is no task for an amateur), the possibilities are enormous. Through the power of wisely supervised, inexpensive credit he may do much to resolve the growing confusion, aid in bringing his clients the indispensable information from government agencies, and raise the standards of land use and management in each community. If our economic system is good enough to defend, it is good enough to be practised realistically.

The principles of good land use and management are simple and general, but their application is a local problem with infinite variations. No one can do it so well as the man on the spot and it ought to be the first responsibility of local agencies which control the flow of credit.

All that we have said thus far leads us to one of the most bedevilled words in our language—education. Clearly enough this means more than the learning acquired in eight or twelve or sixteen years of schooling. It is a lifetime enterprise. Judged by the standards of a less strenuous age, we are doing well enough. The American people are rapidly becoming more conscious of their interdependence with the physical and biological worlds and even of their obligation to conserve its resources. But in this mechanized age we are no longer geared to the leisurely pendulum of grandfather's clock. Events have a way of outstripping knowledge, unless we are prepared for them. One of the most effective educational services in agriculture—agricultural extension as personified by the county agent—has thus been overtaken by the momentum of change. We have already described the resulting improvisation, duplication, and confusion of agencies.

This is not the place to add to the tonnage of discussion on education. Two comments must suffice, both of them reiterations. First, conservation of our resources is not a subject. It is a moral attitude in the employment of technical resources and in our way of living. The old adage, "What you do speaks so loudly I cannot hear what you say," applies here. It follows that those who are to educate us—as children and adults—must be imbued with this moral attitude. If they possess it, it makes little difference what *subject* they expound —the conviction will radiate from them to their audience. I can think of no discipline in the ordinary curriculum—certainly not honest mathematics—which does not involve an opportunity to spread the principles of conservation.

Second, there is a body of knowledge, a point of view, which peculiarly implies all that is meant by conservation, and much more. It is at present neglected in most of our schools. It has been called by H. G. Wells, who cannot be accused of a failure to anticipate events, the science of prophecy. Certainly it is the science of perspective. It is the basis of the philosophy of Jan Smuts, one of the greatest and most humane figures of our day. It is the approach to biological knowledge which is called ecology.

At the close of the preceding chapter, I urged the importance of the trained ecologist in each community, and explained something of the nature of his point of view. The activities of the Soil Conservation Service in numerous districts have, in the meantime, brilliantly exemplified the benefits of the ecologist at work. But this is a subject we cannot wholly delegate to the specialist, any more than we can wholly delegate the care of our bodies. We are all responsible participants in a common enterprise. Unless we have our bearings, even the specialists will fail in their effort to save us.

A young soldier on leave, who had been half-way through his engineering course, complained to Louis Bromfield that his training was too narrow. He said, "I learn about stress and strain and logarithms and nothing about the relation of my job to social problems or history or economics or soil or water or forestry problems. When I have finished my course I'll know everything about building dams and railways and landing fields, but I wish I knew something about their significance or their relation to human society."[1]

[1] Quoted by permission of the author.

What the soldier meant was that when he becomes an engineer he will need the viewpoint which comes with an understanding of ecology if he is to exemplify in his work the social function which alone can give meaning to his great profession, and which mankind so sorely needs.